Survival Kit for New Christians   Presented

My Personal Journey

Name _____

Place I became a Christian _____

Date I became a Christian _____

Date I was baptized into a church fellowship _____

Persons who helped me come to know Christ _____

_____

_____

_____

_____	_____
Date I began work in *Survival Kit for* *New Christians*	Date I completed work in *Survival Kit for* *New Christians*

ISBN 978-0-8054-9683-3
Item 001117185

Dewey Decimal Classification Number: 248.4
Subject: Christian Life / Salvation

Printed in the United States of America

Multi-Language Publishing
LifeWay Resources
One LifeWay Plaza
Nashville, TN 37234-0196

Welcome to the Beginning of a New Life with Jesus Christ!

You made an important decision. Your decision was to trust Jesus Christ to save your life. You believe Jesus is the Son of God. He is the Lord (boss) in your life. This is the biggest decision for your life.

This book is called *Survival Kit for New Christians*. It is written to help you live every day the way Jesus wants you to live. This book can help you grow spiritually and win the fight with sin.

You began a new life when you prayed to God and accepted Jesus as your Savior. The Bible says you were "born again." This means you left your old life behind you. You started a new life with new values and a new way to live every day. You found God's forgiveness. Now you are ready to start learning.

There are may things you want to know. You have a new life. You need food to help you grow. This food is knowing the Bible way to help you grow from the beginning.

First, decide an exact time and place to meet the Lord daily. This is important for self-control. You will not grow spiritually the way you should if you do not do this. Call this time every day your Quiet Time. The place should be the same place every day. The first week of study will help you start a regular Quiet Time.

This book will help you learn and start new habits. These new habits will take time to develop. Sometimes these new habits will conflict with your old habits. This is normal. All of us have experienced it. Your first new habit is to start a daily Quiet Time.

What is in the *Survival Kit*?

There are five Bible principles you will be learning. You can remember them on your hand …

> **the thumb = 1 Body**
> **the forefinger (index finger) = 2 natures**
> **the second finger (middle finger) = 3 aspects of salvation**
> **the third finger (ring finger) = 4 sources of authority**
> **the little finger = 5 & 5 Principle**

The palm of your hand represents Christ living in you, controlling everything. These five Bible principles will be studied in your *Survival Kit*.

The lessons in your *Survival Kit* are planned to help you understand how God works in your life and your world. When you are finished, you will be able to explain many things about the Christian faith to other people.

You face many problems and temptations in everyday life.

This *Survival Kit* will help you understand different parts of your life. It will help you get through them. These things in your *Survival Kit* will help you have a foundation in your Christian life. Activity in other areas of church will help your faith grow on this foundation.

Almost all Christians experience several stages of growth in their Christian life.

1. The Honeymoon Stage
2. The Fight Stage
3. The Doubting Stage
4. The Panic-Search-For-What-Is-Right Stage
5. The "Silent Christian" Stage

The next few pages will explain these stages.

1. The Honeymoon Stage

This is a happy time in your life. You understand you have *new* life. You are excited about it.

You learn during this stage that you are a part of the Body of Christ. You are a member of His Church. This is the time when you are baptized. You show the world that your life now belongs to Jesus Christ.

It is important in this stage to learn that much future growth in your Christian life depends on your relationship to the church.

You will learn in this stage …
Week 1: Christ in You
Week 2: Church Life
Week 3: Church Service

2. The Fight Stage

The honeymoon ends when you have your first fight. You thought things were going well. You are a really good Christian. POW! Suddenly you have problems with frustration, jealousy, or gossip. You feel embarrassed because old problems show up again. You don't want God to be ashamed because you have the same old problems.

Now comes the dangerous part. You think about pretending to be finished with those problems. They are really still there.

You become busy with church work. You think church work will help. You later learn that church work does not help. You feel as a hypocrite feels.

You need to learn an important principle before these things happen. Christ started to live in you when you began your *new life*. The old self (nature) with all the sins did not completely pass away. There are now two natures in you—your old self with the sins and your new self with Christ.

That is the reason you need to learn about …
Week 4: Two Natures—Part One: The New You
Week 5: Two Natures—Part Two: The Old You

NEW NATURE

OLD NATURE

3. The Doubting Stage

Many people begin to *doubt* their salvation if they do not learn the right things. They begin to feel that their salvation is finished. They know they are saved. They feel that is the only important thing.

Jesus promised when you became a Christian that the Holy Spirit would be in you. He would teach you all things (John 14:26). You need more information about salvation when you have conflict in yourself between the old life and the new life.

You need to learn three things about your salvation: it happens at an *exact time;* it is a *process through time* as you control the old you; there is a *final time* when Christ will make you free forever.

The next two weeks you will study …
Week 6: Three Aspects of Salvation—Part One: Its Beginning and End
Week 7: Three Aspects of Salvation—Part Two: The Daily Process

4. The Panic-Search-For-What-Is-Right Stage

You need to learn where to find what is right to be protected from this stage. You also must learn how to compare the truth to other things.

Some people say *thinking* is the way to find the truth. Others say *experience* is the way to find the truth. Another person will say that *church tradition* (habits) is the right answer.

You will learn that the only place to find the truth (authority) and what is right is in the *written Word of God, the Bible.*

The next two weeks you will study …
Week 8: Four Sources of Authority—Part One: Three Weak Sources
Week 9: Four Sources of Authority—Part Two: One Strong Source

5. The "Silent Christian" Stage

Do you know some Christians who never witness? Don't worry if you have not met any. You will meet some Christians who never witness. Why not witness?

1. They feel that other Christians who know more and are more mature should be the people to witness.
2. They don't want to talk about the Christian life when they are not living right.
3. They have a substitute for witnessing. That substitute is church activities that do not require any witnessing. These activities don't require any *spiritual* power or maturity.

Many Christians are in this silent stage.

Christians who do not witness are not effective sharing about Jesus Christ. They may be busy in church. They are not helping anyone become a Christian. Their lives do not influence other people in a positive way for the Lord. You can learn the *5 & 5 Principle* so this does not happen in your Christian life.

This principle means you always have *five* people in you life you can witness to in a natural way. There should also be *five* people you cannot witness to, but you can pray for them. It is exciting to discover that God answers when we pray for people to be saved.

The last two weeks of your will study be …
Week 10: The 5 & 5 Principle—Five You can Win by Prayer
Week 11: The 5 & 5 Principle—Five You can Win by Witnessing

Summary of your *Survival Kit* Material

Week 1: Christ in You

Week 2: Church Life

Week 3: Church Service

Week 4: Two Natures—Part One: The New You

Week 5: Two Natures—Part Two: The Old You

Week 6: Three Aspects of Salvation—Part One: The Beginning and End

Week 7: Three Aspects of Salvation—Part Two, The Daily Process

Week 8: Four Sources of Authority—Part One: Three Weak Sources

Week 9: Four Sources of Authority—Part Two: One Strong Source

Week 10: The 5 & 5 Principle—Five You can Win by Prayer

Week 11: The 5 & 5 Principle—Five You can Win by Witnessing

Week 1: Christ in You

Day 1: How to Establish a Quiet Time

Read 1 John 4:13-15.

Suppose you only eat on Sunday mornings and Wednesday nights. Would your body stay healthy? Of course not! Do you think your spirit will stay healthy if you only feed your spirit on Sunday and Wednesday?

The only way to stay spiritually healthy is to have an everyday Quiet Time with the Lord. You must find time each day to be alone with Christ. You will be happy about what happens. Your spirit will be healthy.

Remember the idea of your hand? The palm means "Christ living in you, controlling everything." A daily Quiet Time is important. It helps you stay in contact with Jesus. Jesus gives you spiritual life. Here are some ideas to help you start a daily Quiet Time.

1. *Have a specific time and place.* A desk or a table beside your bed—any place will be all right. It is important to have 15 minutes to yourself. It is best to start your day with a Quiet Time. Your day will be different because you started with Christ.

2. *Be consistent.* A "sometimes way" shows you are not as serious as you need to be about growing spiritually.

3. *Have ready a Bible, pencil, and paper.* For 11 weeks you will be using the *Survival Kit* for your Quiet Time. Later you will use other materials to help you study the Bible. You might want to use a notebook at that time.

4. *Begin with prayer.* Open your heart and mind to Christ. Ask Him to teach, lead, and discipline you in your Bible study.

5. *End with a specific plan for the day that applies what you read.* Before you end your Quiet Time, decide how your life will be different because of the things you learned in the Bible.

HAVE TODAY'S QUIET TIME NOW.

Pray. Tell God about your love for Him. Thank Him for your many blessings. Tell Him the things you need for God to do in your life. Ask Him to use you and control you in your life today.

Read 1 John 4:13-15 in a version of the Bible you can easily understand. We recommend the *Holman Christian Standard Bible*® (HCSB®).

Be sure you understand what the verses mean. Write the verses in your own words below to be sure you understand them. Don't copy out of the Bible.

_____

_____

_____

_____

Answer these three questions about the verses ...

What did God give you to prove you are saved? (v. 13)

_____

_____

What do Christian people tell other people that shows God is living in them?

_____

_____

What other words are used to tell who Jesus is?

_____

_____

As a Christian you have personally experienced that God sent His Son to be your Savior. How will the things from this verse change your life today? Write one thing you will do today that shows these verses working in your life.

_____

_____

_____

_____

_____

Week 1: Christ in You

Day 2: Using Your Bible for Christian Growth

Read Psalm 119:11,15-16; 40:8.

You will be given a few Bible verses every day to study. Your daily Quiet Time should always focus on the Bible. Do you have a good Bible to study with? It is important that you have a Bible you can understand clearly. We will base our study on the *Holman Christian Standard Bible®* (HCSB®).

Turn to the Contents (Index) in the front of your Bible. This will help you find the books you want.

Find Psalm 119. Read verse 11. Where did the writer keep the Word of God?

_____

One way to say *memorized* is to say "I know it by heart." The writer used the word *heart* to explain where he keeps God's Word. The last part of the verse tells the reason to keep God's Word in our hearts. What is that reason?

_____

Memorizing God's Word can help you avoid sinning against God.

Read Psalm 40:8. Where can you keep verses for emergencies if you don't have a Bible with you?

_____

Go back to Psalm 119. Read verses 15-16. What feelings will you have as you learn to memorize Bible verses?

_____

It is wonderful to know that you will have delight and joy when you memorize God's Word! Don't think you can't memorize. You have already memorized many things. Circle the things you have already memorized in the list below.

Telephone Numbers	Street Names	House Addresses
Zip Codes	Word Spelling	Mathematics
People's Names	Poems	Book Titles
Future Dates	License Numbers	
Social Security Numbers	Scripture Verses	

No other word of advice will have as much value as this. Memorize Scripture on a regular schedule. There are two verses at the end of this material to help you start. The first verse is Psalm 119:11. You have already read and studied it. You should memorize two verses each week.

Why learn to memorize Bible verses?
1. It is easier to remember a verse exactly than in general.
2. Memorized verses help you resist sin.
3. It helps you tell other people about Jesus.
4. It is used to explain things you believe.

Start now! Carry the verses with you. Start with one verse on Monday. Then start the second verse on Wednesday.

Write the verses. Put them in places you can see every day like the refrigerator door, the bathroom mirror, the steering wheel of your car, or beside your bed.

You will find that with practice you can use every little bit of time to help you memorize your verses.

Learn your verses like your spiritual growth depends on it … because it does.

Week 1: Christ in You

Day 3: Learning to Pray

Read Matthew 6:9-13.

Maybe you have met Christians who never want to pray in a public place. You will learn to pray, if you don't yet. Praying (public or private) is a simple thing.

Do you have a problem talking with your close friends? No, of course not! You will never have a problem talking to our Lord. He wants you to talk to Him as a child would talk to a father. Be free to share with Him your attitudes, fears, wants, and frustrations. He will understand. He will answer your prayers.

Jesus' followers asked Him ho to pray. He gave them an example prayer that is often called the Model Prayer (Lord's prayer). Find Matthew 6:9-13. Copy the prayer below. Match each part of the prayer with the sentences.

Topics in Model Prayer   The Model Prayer

Starting Right   _____

                               _____

Showing Respect for
God's Name   _____

                               _____

Giving Ourselves and   _____
all on Earth to God's Plan
                               _____

                               _____

Asking God to Provide Our   _____
Needs (Not our Wants)
                               _____

Asking God for Forgiveness   _____

                               _____

                               _____

Asking God for Protection   _____

                               _____

                               _____

                               _____

Saying God's Control of Us   _____
Is Our Biggest Wish
                               _____

                               _____

Ending Rightly   _____

Do you understand the Model Prayer (Lord's Prayer) better now? The best way to learn how to pray is to do it. Fill out these sentences to help you in your prayer today.

Now check how you matched phrases and sentences in Jesus' Model Prayer with the outline of topics in that prayer. Look at the verses of Matthew 6:9-13 in your Bible. Compare them with the verse numbers printed below. You should have matched each topic with all or part of the verse marked beside the topic in the outline.

Starting Right (v. 9)

Showing Respect for God's Name (v. 9)

Giving Ourselves and All On Earth to God's Plans (v. 10)

Asking God to Provide Our Needs (Not Our Wants) (v. 11)

Asking God for Forgiveness (v. 12)

Asking God for Protection (v. 13)

Saying God's Control of us is our Biggest Wish (v. 13)

Ending Rightly (v. 13)

Does Matthew 6:9-13 seem clearer to you now that you have matched what it says with topics in the outline? You can see from this outline that any major element of Jesus' Model Prayer could become a prayer all by itself. At times you will need to ask God for forgiveness, or for protection, or for provision to meet your needs. At other times you will wish to declare Him Lord and commit yourself to His will for your life.

The best way to learn how to pray is … to pray! To collect your thoughts in praying, you may find it helpful to finish these sentences.

I praise You today, Lord, for _____

I promise myself to do today _____

I need to ask You, Lord, about _____

I need to share my desire for _____

I say that you are in _____

It doesn't matter if you finish all of the sentences or not. You can still pray. Use your outline of the Lord's Prayer and pray—now.

Week 1: Christ in You

Day 4: Understanding What has Happened to You

Read 2 Corinthians 5:17; Colossians 1:21-22,27.

You should understand that there are some things changing in your life as you develop your Quiet Time day by day. The second memory verse for this week explains some of these changes. Read 2 Corinthians 5:17 again.

Fill in the blanks.

Your _____ life/things are passing away.

Your _____ life/things are beginning.

All of these changes are made by _____ .

Yes, Christ makes the difference between your old and new life.

Find and read Colossians 1:21-22 now. Answer the questions.

What was your attitude about God before you accepted Christ and became a Christian?

_____

_____

Because you and God were enemies, you did things that were

_____

Now you are learning that some things you did when you were not a Christian are no fun. God is changing you! He is making you

_____

Holy means that you are set apart for God's use and no one else's. Second Corinthians 5:17 explains that a different way. Write all of the verse you can remember. Don't look it up. Try to do it from memory.

_____

_____

_____

_____

Read Colossians 1:27. Where is Christ now?

_____

Remember discussing the hand? Write what the palm of the hand represents:

_____

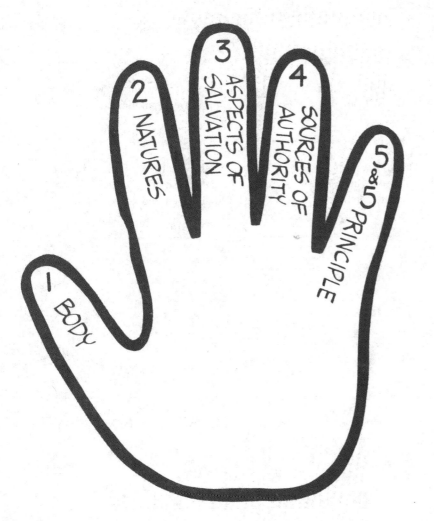

Habits are hard to break. The silliest thing we can do is to continue a habit that is no more fun. And you don't enjoy them any more. Don't let habits you don't enjoy any more continue as God changes your feelings about them. Let God help you take the old habits out of your life. List some old habits that you do not enjoy now.

_____   _____

_____   _____

_____   _____

Don't try to reduce bad habits, stop them. Quit them when Christ takes away the desire for a habit.

Other habits may be harmful, not enjoyable. Stop doing those things as well.

Day 5: A Basic Principle to Live By

Read 1 Corinthians 10:31; Romans 14:7-8.

The Christian religion does not have a long list of do's and don'ts for you to follow.

Instead of a long list, there is a simple principle to follow. It is said clearly in 1 Corinthians 10:31. Find and read that verse and then write it here:

_____

_____

_____

_____

Now read Romans 14:7-8. These verses make it clear that we should:
• Have behavior that shows our new life with Christ.
• Do everything to bring glory to God.

Example: During dinner, your friend brings a bottle of wine to the table and wants you to drink a glass with him. What do you do?
  A. Take a small drink and then no more.
  B. Scold the friend for drinking wine.
  C. Avoid facing it and make up an excuse.
  D. Explain that you are now a Christian. Tell your friend that God has taken away your want for a drink of wine.

Which one brings glory to God? _____

I hope you chose the last one. It is the best one to bring glory to Him.

Life is full of choices like this example. It is best to always act in ways that show Christ living in you and controlling you. You do not have to act like a strange person to do this. You should have a gentle and loving expression. People will respect you for that attitude.

You know that one way to help us with those situations is to know Bible verses. Write Psalm 119: 11 here.

_____

_____

Maybe you'd like to write your own Scripture memory cards. Writing the verses word for word is another good way to help you learn more quickly.

Have you finished memorizing your other verse (2 Corinthians 5:17) for this week? Try to write it too.

_____

_____

_____

_____

Reviewing 2 Corinthians 5:17 should make it easy for you to fill in what is missing on the hand.

Remember: This hand with its fingers and palm is a simple way to recall everything you will learn in your *Survival Kit*. Fill in what should be written on the hand itself.

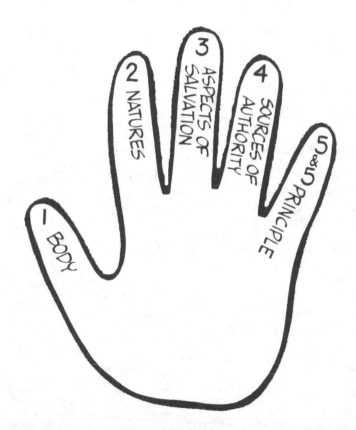

Did you write *Christ living in you, controlling everything*? Much more important … do you now know and feel more of Christ living in you than you did a week ago?

The following weeks of this *Survival Kit* will not tell you day by day to have a Quiet Time. But you have already discovered for yourself how much a Quiet Time can mean in your spiritual growth as a new Christian. Each day's material in the *Survival Kit* will always include some Scripture verses for you to read and study, five days a week. During your Quiet Time on the sixth and seventh day of each week, use your Sunday School lesson, your Discipleship material, or other Bible passages.

Don't forget to pray as you memorize and think about God's Word. A daily time of prayer and Bible study can be the best way for Christ to live in and control your life.

Week 2: Church Life

Day 1: One Body

Read Romans 12:4-5; 1 Corinthians 12:12-13.

Your spiritual growth depends on your being involved with the Body of Christ (the Church). There should not be any "Lone Ranger" Christians in God's family. You give your life to Christ and to other people who are also Christians when you become a Christian.

Sometimes a family does not have a baby. But can you imagine a baby staying alive without a family to take care of it?

Babies cannot live without families. They need love, attention, and everything given to them. A baby to survive must have a family—people who are concerned about its survival. The same is true for Christians. You will not grow spiritually without the family of God. The family of God is called by several names: *Church, called-out ones, Body of Christ,* and *living stones.* (You will learn more about these names later.)

Open your Bible to Romans 12:4-5. These verses give one main idea about the family of God (the Church). That idea can be written like a math problem. Fill in the missing letters below, learning from what you read in Romans 12:4-5.

M ___ ___ ___   M ___ ___ ___ ___ ___ (or parts) =
1 ___ ___ ___ ___

An important idea about the church is its unity. The Bible says, "We are one body in Christ." The answer should be like this:

Many Members (or parts) = 1 Body

Do you remember what you have learned about the palm and fingers? This will help you remember the materials in this *Survival Kit.*

The **thumb** represents _____ .

The **palm** represents _____

It is interesting to see the meanings together here. "Christ living in you, controlling everything" means Christ lives in you. You are a Christian. He lives in every Christian. So all of us together make the one Body of Christ. Christ is in us. We are in Christ. We are "one body in Christ."

The main point about the one Body of Christ is like the thumb on your hand. The thumb works with each finger. The church works the same way with all of the other ideas you will learn. You must always mix the first idea, the Body, with the other ideas to become a growing, happy Christian.

Romans 12:4-5 that you just read is one of your memory verses for this week. Write the verses below.

_____

_____

_____

_____

There are four important words in Romans 12:4-5 for today's study: "many parts," "one" "body". Each of us has one body with many parts. These parts do not all have the same function. We are many Christians and in Christ we form one body.

Now find 1 Corinthians 12:12-13 in your Bible. Read it carefully. What verse is the most like Romans 12:4-5? It is verse _____

You see the same four important words in 1 Corinthians 12:12-13 as in Romans 12:4-5. Write them to make this right.

_____   _____ =

_____   _____

Remember that " many parts" make "one body". Now look at verse 13. What was one of the first things the Holy Spirit did to you when you become a Christian?

_____

The word *baptized* in 1 Corinthians 12:13 means fully in over your head. The Holy Spirit puts you fully in church over your head.

You must be deeply involved in your church if you will have a natural, healthy spiritual life. You will find in a church the things you need for spiritual growth.

You should stand and tell people in your church that you have faith Christ and have asked for forgiveness for your sins. You have been baptized in water in your church. You should do that as soon as soon as possible. Don't think you have a choice about church. You cannot postpone it. It is the first step to survival as a growing Christian.

Week 2: Church Life

Day 2: The Church, A Body

Read 2 Timothy 1:8-10; 1 Peter 2:9-10; Ephesians 4:1-4.

Do you know what the word *church* means? It translates a Greek word from one of the languages of the Bible. *Ekklesia* means people who are "called out" from other people.

Imagine a large group of people. All of them live the way they want to live. They do whatever they want to do. Christ comes to them. He says, "Follow Me! Be separate from other people and become my disciples."

Some people notice, but they don't pay attention. Others decide to follow. They come to Christ.

These are called the "called-out people." They are the Church.

You will see the words *called* and *calling* in all three of the Bible passages you are to read for today. First read 2 Timothy 1:8-10. Find the answers to these questions.

Who calls us? _____

In whom are we called? _____

God calls us out in Christ Jesus. Does this remind you of one of the verses you learned last week? Write 2 Corinthians 5:17 in the spaces.

_____

_____

_____

Find the verse in your Bible if you need to check your memory.

Now read 1 Peter 2:9-10. These verses tell us what Christian are supposed to do. What is it?

_____

_____

We are supposed to tell others how God has called us and saved us. We are supposed to tell people about our Lord.

List several of the titles 1 Peter 2:9-10 gives to people who are "called out".

(v. 9) _____

(v. 9) _____

(v. 9) _____

(v. 9) _____

(v. 10) _____

The people of God are explained in Ephesians 4:1-4. Find and read these verses now. List here some things the people of God should do.

_____

_____

_____

They way Christ wants us to live is clear. Humility, gentleness, patience, love—these things will sow in the lives of people whom God has called.

Which things do you want to show the most in your life today? Put a circle around the one you want the most.

Think about this: Christ does not give you these things; Christ is these things. Christ is humble, gentle, patient, and all the other things. You will show these things to other people when you let Christ be Lord and live in you.

Did you notice a two-word idea in Ephesians 4:4 you have seen before? That is "one body." Tomorrow you will continue to think about this idea.

You have finished memorizing another verse that tells you about "one body." That is Romans 12:4-5. Write as much as you can remember here.

_____

_____

_____

_____

Be sure to check the verse in your Bible. Be sure you remember this verse right. Don't waste time memorizing a mistake.

Week 2: Church Life

Day 3: No Divisions in the Body

Read 1 Corinthians 2:14-27.

People used stories many times in the Bible to help other people understand the point. Jesus used stories called parables. Paul also used stories. The Bible reading for today is a story Paul told.

Paul in 1 Corinthians 12:14-27 compared Christ's called-out people to parts of a human body. Each part is special and different. It is also connected to the other parts of the body. No part of the body can live without the help of the other parts.

A hand cannot live in the air alone. It must have an arm. There cannot be division in Christ's body (the Church). There is no reason for jealousy. (Can you imagine your hand jealous because of the ear?)

A man wrote to his friend: "Pardon my handwriting. I have a bad case of gout in my foot." Only people who have experienced gout can now how pain in the foot can affect the handwriting.

Each part of the body is related to one another. Each affects one another. Your growth in the Christian life is related to other people in the Body of Christ. All hurt when one suffers. All are happy when one rejoices

That is the reason baptism and the Lord's Supper are celebrated when all the members of the church are together. All members celebrate together when we witness a baptism. All members in the Lord's Supper share memory with you of the Lord's death to give us new life. These are part of the life of the Body of Christ. They cannot be enjoyed by any who are not a part of the body.

How much do you know about baptism and the Lord's Supper? Stop now. Read the material below. Maybe you prefer to finish and come back later. That is fine, too.

Baptism and the Lord's Supper

Write **B** for **baptism** and **LS** for **Lord's Supper** beside each of the following:

_____ 1. Described in 1 Corinthians 11:23-26.
_____ 2. Described in Romans 6:4.
_____ 3. Experienced personally by a Christian one time only.
_____ 4.. Experienced by a Christian many times.
_____ 5. Shows Jesus' broken body and shed blood.
_____ 6. Shows Jesus' death and resurrection.
_____ 7. Shows a person's death to sin and new life in Christ.
_____ 8. Commanded to be done by al who follow Christ.
_____ 9. Described as one of the ordinances of the church.

Answers: 1-LS; 2-B; 3-B; 4-LS; 5-LS; 6-B; 7- -either or both; 9-either.

Read carefully 1 Corinthians 12:18. Who decides where each member of the body belongs? _____

Did you notice that 1 Corinthians 12:18 is the second memory verse for this week? Today the week is half finished. You should start memory work on the second verse today.

You may sometimes wish you were some other person. You may wish you could do things other church members could do. But there is no reason to be jealous of any other member of the body. God put you exactly where He wants you to be. Think about that as you memorize 1 Corinthians 12:18.

Now read slowly 1 Corinthians 12:25-27 one more time. Think about what it means. Here are two questions for you to think about from these verses.

1. Are Christians people in the church the only people who live like these verses say? Is it common to find this same way to live in people who are not Christian?

_____

_____

2. "Culture shock" is the experience people have when they are in a group of people who have new ways to talk (languages). They have new ways of doing things and new thinking. All are different from the way they are used to/ What "culture shock" did you have when you first become an important part of the church? (Think deeply before answering.)

_____

_____

(Maybe you want to pray about these things in your Quiet Time even if you don't write answers to them.)

Day 4: The Church, A Building

Read 1 Peter 2:1-10; Ephesians 2:19-22.

You already know the Bible uses several different names to describe the Church. One of the most important names is the one you use when you look at your thumb.

The church is _____ in Christ.

You are learning two Bible verses that talk about "1 Body" made up of all people who follow Christ. Write the verses below.

_____

_____

_____

_____

(Romans 12:4-5)

_____

_____

(1 Corinthians 12:18)

Read the verses in 1 Peter 2:1-10 and Ephesians 2:19-22. How do these verses describe the Church?

Christ is the "head of the Body, the Church" (Colossians 1:18). He is also the chief cornerstone of the building. We are each living stones that are being used to build a spiritual house, a holy temple.

The builders must cut and shape stones where they use them. The stone must fit with the other stones. This shows a reason you must be a part of a church to grow properly. God is shaping your life. This means you must fit with other living stones, people.

Read 1 Peter 2:1. What are some things God may want to cut away from your life? Write them below and on the next page.

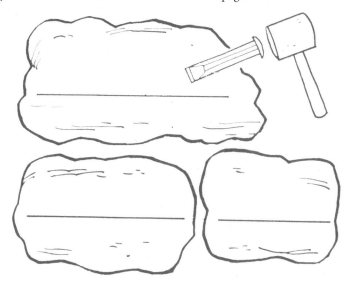

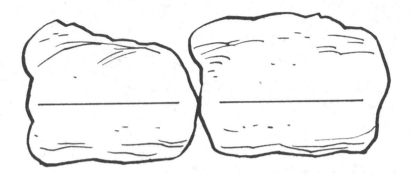

Two kinds of stones are mentioned in 1 Peter 2:1-10. You and I are like rough stones that need some cutting and shaping. But Jesus Christ, our Lord and Savior, is the chosen and precious cornerstone. (See v. 6.)

Read verses 7-8. What kind of stone is Christ to people who refuse to believe in Him?

_____

It may fell strange to think about Christ causing men to stumble. That is what happens when people reject Him.

Now look again at Ephesians 2:19-22. What joins Christians together to make up the Church?

_____

Christ Jesus joins us together. Read verse 22. Why are we joined together?

_____

It is a great thought to know we are being joined together as a building for God's Spirit to live in. Are you beginning to understand how much you need the other Christians to help you grow properly? List two parts of your spiritual life that will not grow without fellowship with other Christians.

_____

_____

Pray about the two things you wrote today during your Quiet Time. Ask God to help you grow in relationship to other believers.

Also, don't forget to review all four of the verses you have memorized in the previous two weeks. Place a check mark beside each one you can say right now.

Psalm 119:11 _____

2 Corinthians 5:17 _____

Romans 12:4-5 _____

1 Corinthians 12:18 _____

Week 2: Church Life

Day 5: New Life in the Body

Read Acts 2:42-47; 4:32-35.

Acts 2	Acts 4	
44	32	Church members are _____ / _____ in Christ.
45	34-34	Church members should _____ their lives.
42-43	33	Church members should _____ their Lord.

These verses cause many people to be confused. Then they learn for themselves the true meaning for the word church. These verses do not teach us to live together. They do not say that all Christians should sell their things and give their money to the poor people. The verses do say that sometimes the people in the church sold some of their things. They shared their money with other people in the church who had serious needs.

Notice, also, they shared more than their money. They shared their lives with one another—eating, praying, sharing in Bible study, and teaching. Their life was proof that they had been "called out" form other people. They did not have a closed and selfish attitude like non-Christians. They had a special family life together.

Remember: This is the thumb of your *Survival Kit* hand. Christ's Church is "1 Body." The thumb must work together with each of the fingers. The fellowship your share with other people is important to your growth in Christ. Do not ignore it. Become deeply involved with your brothers and sisters in the Lord.

Now compare the verses in Acts 2:42-47 and in Acts 4:32-35. Both of them have important things to teach us about the church. Try to finish the sentences that follow.

Maybe you had a hard time remembering that church members are one Body in Christ. You recently read that church members should share their lives. What did you write on the third line? *Proclaim? Witness for? Tell people about?* Any of these would be right.

Read Acts 2:45 one more time. Which is hardest for you to do? Is it hardest to sell something to help a poor church member? Or is it harder for other people to sell things to help you? Why do you think it is harder?

_____

_____

_____

_____

_____

There is no right answer. This is a question to help you think.

Now try this question. Acts 2:46 says that people often visited in one another's homes. How can you follow the Bible and do the same things today?

_____

_____

_____

Now you have a test. Remember the hand? Write what the thumb and the palm represent. Now write them on the hand.

Thumb: _____

Palm: _____

_____

Write 1 Corinthians 12:18. This is one of your memory verses about the Church as one Body in Christ.

_____

_____

Write Psalm 119:11. This is your memory verse that tells you why it is important to learn God's Word by memory.

_____

_____

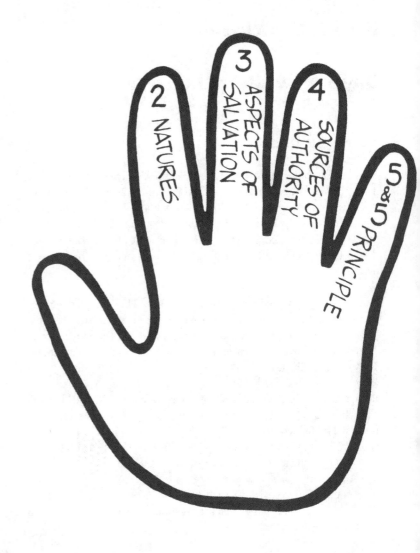

Week 3: Church Service

Day 1: One Body—Made for Love

Read 1 Corinthians 13:1-13.

You have read a beautiful chapter about love. These verses are famous. They discuss the greatest thing in the world.

What is the greatest thing in the world that these verses talk about? It is _____ . In the Kings James Version of the Bible, it is called *charity*. The word is *love* in most other versions.

Love is the greatest thing in the world. God is that love. Christ lives in you to give that love to other people. The Body of Christ (church) is made to show love. People are "called out" to let Christ's love change their lives. Every day His love causes you to become more like Christ.

Now read 1 Corinthians 13 again. This is sometimes called the love chapter. Which of the list is not as good as love.

_____ Great knowledge about spiritual things.
_____ Wonderful speaking skills.
_____ Being willing to die for truth.
_____ Giving a lot to poor people.
_____ Strong faith.
_____ All of these.

Did you understand that all of these are mentioned in 1 Corinthians 13:1-3? Maybe you checked the last line. Maybe you checked all of the lines. Remember: The point is that all of these things are good. But they are not as good as love.

Read 1 Corinthians 13:4-7 again. List the many positive things Paul said about love.

_____

_____

_____

_____

_____

_____

Which one do you want the most in your life? Write your initials beside it.

Surprise! All of these are yours. You are a Christian. God is love. And the Son of God, Christ living in you, will make these things stronger and stronger in your life as you let Him control you.

Write the verse number beside the picture Paul used to talk about us.
_____ A person looking in the mirror.
_____ A baby becoming a man.

Verse 12 describes our limited knowledge about things as being like a person looking in a dirty mirror. Verse 11 compares it to baby talk. That is the reason that knowledge is not equal to love.

Paul listed in 1 Corinthians 13:8, 13 five things that are not love. Write an *X* beside the things that do not stay as long as love. Put a ✔ beside the things that are not as great as love.

_____ Prophecy   _____ Faith
_____ Tongues   _____ Hope
_____ Knowledge

Prophecy, tongues, and knowledge will stop (pass away). (Did you put an *X*?) Faith and hope are great. They are not as great as love. (Did you put a ✔ beside them?) Love is the greatest thing in the world. That is the reason God wants His love to go through you to other people.

God made you a working member of the church when He added you to the Church (His Body). He gave you spiritual skills called gifts. The gifts are like learning a new skill. The more you practice, the better you become. As God uses you to love other people, then your skills become better and better. Their purpose is to let more of Christ's love go through you to other people. Your "work" for Him is to become a way for Him to love people. That is the reason He gave you skills.

The most important thing to remember about gifts is that they are ways for you to show Christ's love. You should not ignore your gifts (skills). You should not focus on them either. Gifts are important only if you are letting Christ's love show through them.

This is clear in your first memory verse for this week. It is 1 Peter 4:10. Read it now.

Tomorrow and all week we will be learning more about how to use our gifts to help one another.

Week 3: Church Service

Day 2: Every Member Has a Job

Read 1 Corinthians 12:4-7; Ephesians 4:11-6.

A leg that does not work right causes the entire body to be crippled. A gland that does not work right can kill the body. The Bible is clear that every member of a Body of Christ (local church) has a job!

God added you to the church to become a working member of it. He gave you spiritual skills called gifts when He put in you the church. You can and should begin to use some of these gifts (skills) immediately. You will not begin to use some gifts God has given you until you become mature. Christ will show you when to use more of your gifts as you become obedient to Christ.

There is a difference between gifts and talents. A *gift* is a spiritual skill that only Christians have. Many people who are not Christians have *talents*. Example: Sign language signing is a talent that can be used for God or for people. It is not a spiritual gift. Faith is a spiritual gift (skill). It is used to give God glory.

List some of your talents. _____

_____

_____

You have been learning some Bible verses that talk about the same thing you read today. Romans 12:4-5 says that everybody in the church has a job. Write that memory verse from last week.

_____

_____

_____

Yesterday you started to memorize a new verse about the gift God has give you. You learned how you can use it to help other people. Write as much as you can of 1 Peter 4:10 below.

_____

_____

Be sure to check your memorization of the verses so that you don't memorize them incorrectly.

Now read another part of the Bible that talks about gifts. It is 1 Corinthians 12:4-6. After you read the verses, finish the chart below.

1 Corinthians 12	Different	The Same
Verse 4	Gifts	Spirit
Verse 5		
Verse 6		

All of the words in the "Different" part should be about the gifts (skills). All of the words in "The Same" part should be about God because He gives us the gifts.

Why does God give us the gifts? The reason is in 1 Corinthians 12:7. Read the verse and put a check mark beside the right answer.

_____ For the benefit of the person who gets the gift.

_____ For the benefit of all people in the church.

You should put a check beside the second one.

Now read some other important verses about the church. Read Ephesians 4:11-16 below:

11 And He personally gave some to be apostles, some prophets, some evangelists, some pastors and teachers,

12 for the training of the saints in the work of ministry, to build up the Body of Christ,

13 until we all reach unity in the faith and in the knowledge of God's Son, [growing] into a mature man with a stature measured by Christ's fullness.

14 Then we will no longer be little children, tossed by the waves and blown around by every wind of teaching, by human cunning with cleverness in the techniques of deceit.

15 But speaking the truth in love, let us grow in every way into Him who is the head-Christ.

16 From Him the whole body, fitted and knit together by every supporting ligament, promotes the growth of the body for building up itself in love by the proper working of each individual part.

Underline every sentence in these verses that helps you understand that it is important for you to experience spiritual growth. (You should be able to find five or six, maybe more.)

Do you see in Ephesians 4:16 what responsibility members of the church have for one another?

_____

Did you notice that we are to do everything "in love"?

Week 3: Church Service

Day 3: Gifts

Read Romans 12:1-8; 1 Peter 1:13-16.

God has given you may spiritual gifts. You must prove that you will obey Christ before you can use your gifts. Do you let yourself be used by Christ for loving other people? Other gifts will appear as you let Christ love other people through you so that you can continue to love. The way to get these gifts is through obeying Christ.

The Lord is wise enough that He does not give you gifts until you are mature to use them. But, there are two gifts that we believe every Christian has. What do you think these gifts are? You read about them in Romans 12:1-8.

Look at the spiritual gifts listed in Romans 12:1-8. Choose and write two you think you have and can use now.

(1) The gift of _____. (2) The gift of _____.

It doesn't matter how poor with money you feel or how rich. You can still give and serve for Christ's benefit. Did you list these two gifts? You have every reason to believe God has given you these two gifts. You can use them now. We know God expects every Christian to give and to serve. We can know He has given us these gifts.

The gift of giving is talked about in Romans 12:8. The gift of service is talked about in Romans 12:7. The gift of giving also is in 2 Corinthians 9:7. This is the second verse you should memorize this week. Read that verse now.

What kind of giver does God love? A _____ giver.

Remember the title for today. The way to get and use the gifts is obedience. God gives gifts to the people He can trust to use them for Him.

Read Romans 12:1-3 again to help you understand what obedience requires. Here are some important words from these verses.

Be transformed   **Be conformed**
Present a sacrifice   **Discern the will of God**

One of these words in Romans 12:1-3 says what we must not do if you are obeying God. The other three say what you must do. Try to write these four correctly.

What you must not do: _____

What you must do: _____

_____

_____

Answers.
What you must not do: Be conformed to this age.
What you must do: Give yourself as a living sacrifice.
Be transformed (by the living Christ).
Do the will of God.

First Peter 1:13-16 also talks about obedience. Read those verses now. What are you supposed to turn from in verse 14 ?

_____

You might have written the desires of your former life. The desires are caused by ignorance (not knowing) as when we lived without Jesus Christ.

But now you know. Christ living in you and controlling you helps you know God's plan. You are learning as a member of the church more about what Christ wants you to become. The same word is used four times in 1 Peter 1:15-16. What is that word?

_____

Why is holy living important to a person to whom God has given gifts?

_____

_____

_____

Can you imagine what would happen if a person tried to use God's gift the wrong way? Now here is another question you can think about. Do you struggle with the idea of being obedient to Christ? Can you list some reasons for the struggle? What parts of your life are having to change that you are struggling with?

_____

_____

_____

Week 3: Church Service

Day 4: The Gift of Service

Read 1 Corinthians 1:4-8; 16:15-16; Acts 9:36-42.

You have two gifts that God has given you to show other people Christ's love.

1. The gift of _____. 2. The gift of _____.

Romans 12:7-8 talks about the gift of service and the gift of giving. Romans 12:6 talks about "we have different gifts" that God has given us. Who decides what fits each person in the church should get? You should remember from your memory verse last week. It is 1 Corinthians 12:18. Can you write it on these lines?

_____

_____

Check to be sure you remember 1 Corinthians 12:18. See if you can say 1 Peter 4:10 and 2 Corinthians 9:7 from memory. These are your two verses for this week.

Read these two Bible passages. Put an X beside the ones that talk about the gift of service or ministry.

_____ 1 Corinthians 1:4-8   _____ 1 Corinthians 16:15-16

The gift of service in 1 Corinthians 16:15-16 is sometimes called the gift of administration. The word really means a person that serves at tables (a waiter). It is used to describe any activity that we do because of Christ's love working in us.

Serving the Lord in simple things is obedience. Christ was willing to wash the feet for His disciples. The same Christ is now Lord of your life. How can you expect him to give you bigger things to do if you are not faithful to Him in small things?

Read 1 Corinthians 1:4-8. Do you get the idea that you have some of these of these gifts as soon as you accept Jesus Christ as your Savior? The "waiting" is for Jesus to come the second time, not for gifts.

Read 1 Corinthians 16:15-16. These verses say that the Stephenas's family is doing a job. What job are they doing?

_____

Whom were they serving? _____

The word *saints* (1 Corinthians 16:15) means Christians, the called-out people, not just people that are "super Christians." How do these verses say we are to act to people who are using the gift of service?

_____

_____

We are supposed to follow those people who are using the gift of service. Now read a beautiful story about another Christian who used the gift of service. Read Acts 9:36-42. How did Dorcas use her gifts?

_____

You have the gift of service. You may not use it by sewing for widows, as Dorcas did. But you do have the gift of service. Christ's living in you will first teach you the importance of serving other people. The gift will be the foundation for all of your ministry in the church now and in the future. You can begin to use it today.

Pray about the answer to this question. In what way today does Christ want you to serve other people in the church?

_____ ,

Now do some checking on yourself. How are you doing as a Christian? You have the Lord's promise (John 10:28) that you will never lose your relationship with Christ. It is good to check on yourself sometimes.

You have been using your *Survival Kit* for almost three weeks now. How may days in the three weeks have you had a Quiet Time? Did it include prayer and Bible study? Write the number of days.

_____

How many Bible verses have you memorized? Underline the verses you can say now.

Psalm 119:11   Romans 12:4-5   1 Peter 4:10

2 Corinthians 5:17   1 Corinthians 12:18   2 Corinthians 9:7

Remember the hand and fingers? The palm is _____

_____

The thumb is _____ .

If you need to check your answers, look in the first part of this *Survival Kit.*

Do you realize more about Christ living in you and controlling you than you did three weeks ago?

Yes ❑   **No** ❑

Are Bible study and prayer more important to you now than they were three weeks ago?

Yes ❑   **No** ❑

Are you becoming closer in your relationship with other church members?

Yes ❑   **No** ❑

I encourage you to do something about it if you answered "no" to any of these questions. Find help from your pastor or a friend. Pray and ask God to show you His will for your life.

Week 3: Church Service

Day 5: The Gift of Giving

Read 2 Corinthians 8:1-5; 9:6-15.

You have two spiritual gifts you can use now. Both gifts (skills) are ways you can let Christ's love show through you.

Yesterday you learned about the gift of _____ .

The gift of giving, like the gift of service, is part of the way Christ lets His love show through a person. This kind of love helps the needs of the Body (church), not just support of special activities.

Don't misunderstand and think that giving is only a gift God gives to rich people. It is a gift to be used by all believers.

"Giving" is a Bible word to explain a person's planning to allow someone else to own something that he now owns. Giving is a change of ownership. This happens because of the Holy Spirit's working in us. When you realize Jesus owns everything you have, it is not hard to let something go to meet the needs of His Body, the Church. You will have problems only when you continue to think something is yours. The way to be successful is to let the Holy Spirit lead you to give what you have. You do this, believing faithfully that God will

Read 2 Corinthians 8:1-5. Do you think Christians in these verses could afford to give a lot? Why or why not?

_____

Did you write words like *poor, poverty, trouble?* Members of the church in Macedonia were not rich, but they gave.

There is one verse you should know by memory before you read the next chapter in 2 Corinthians. Can you write 2 Corinthians 9:7 on these lines?

_____

_____

_____

(Be sure to check your memorization.)

Now read 2 Corinthians 9:6-15. What two verses in verses 6-10 talk strongly about God's taking care of your giving? Verse _____ and verse _____.

Verses 8 and 10 give the answers. What is the reason in verse 11 for God giving to you?

_____

Your giving is possible because God gives to you. Many people will thank God because of your giving. Second Corinthians 9:13 says that other people will see the giving and will know you are really Christians. Who will get the biggest blessing from your using the gift of giving?

_____

Many people will give glory to God because Christians give to help one another. What commitment (promise) does Christ want you to make as you use this gift of giving? (Remember: He is more interested in your giving to bey Him than in how much you give.)

You become mature in your special gifts when you let Christ use them. You will soon learn that there are other spiritual gifts in your life. God gives them so that your service might increase in showing His love to other people.

You had a hand that could do nothing when you were born. You later learned how to hold things. Later again your hand became more mature and learned to write. Then your mind learned to control you hand to work together to write a letter or in a book. Your hands are now skilled tools. They are able to do many things your mind tells them to do.

You become mature through some activities as a member in the Body of Christ (Church). You find more things ready for you to do after you are matured. Christ will show you other gifts (skills) that you have as you learn to use the gifts of giving and serving. He will show you what He has given you to increase His love showing and working through you to other people.

All of these things depend on one thing—your obedience to Christ! The way to continue growing as you mature is to continue to obey Him. Serve and give. Use your spiritual gifts and skills. It will become clear that Christ is the person who gives you the abilities. He is the one who lives in you and loves through you. The other things depend on God's plan for you.

Just use for now what you have. Trust the Master (Christ) for the other things. This is a brief study about these things. You will want to learn in the months and the years in the future much more about the spiritual gifts.*

What you need to do now is to focus on the next part of your *Survival Kit*. Two natures (personalities) live in you. Learn about them now. They will be with you for the rest of your life.

---

*This Gift Is Mine by Ralph W. Neighbour, Jr. (Broadman Press, 1974) is recommended for your study later.

Week 4: Two Natures—
Part One: The New You

Day 1: The New Nature

Read Galatians 5:13-18.

Did you know you have two natures (personalities or selves) now?

You have had the old nature since you were born. You have a new nature since your new birth (you became a Christian). One nature is elfish and wants honor for itself. The other natures tries to permit God's love to show through you.

Your Bible study, starting now and in the future, will teach you new things about these two natures. You have lived with your old nature (selfish) for al of your life. You do not need to learn about it first. This week you will study what the Bible teaches about your new nature.

The old nature in you is like gravity. Gravity pulls things down. It always works. You cannot fly or even float off the ground because gravity. Your old nature holds you down.

The new law is like the wings on an airplane. It causes the airplane to fly as the wing moves through the air. This always works if everything is done right. The airplane will fly as long as you follow the right directions. The new nature works in your life to cause God's love to go through you

and to help you win the struggle with sin. The old nature will pull you down anytime you do not allow the new nature to work in your life.

Find and read Galatians 5:13-18. You will see in verses 13-14 an important word used two times. It is a word you have studied more than once in your *Survival Kit*. This word tells how your new nature works in your life as a Christian. What is that word?

_____

_____

One way your new nature works in love is through using one of your gifts, the gift of giving. Do you remember the verse you learned last week about the kind of giver God loves. Write here 2 Corinthians 9:7.

_____

_____

_____

Yes, your new nature works in love. But not your old nature. There are some things in Galatians 5:15 that show the old nature is in control. What are those things?

_____

_____

Paul talked about people hurting one another in Galatians 5:15. It is terrible to see people acting that way. Paul explained in verse 17 how that can happen.

Read the verses again but change *Spirit* to *new nature*. Do you understand after reading the verse this way that it is your decision about which nature will be in control of your life? Choosing either nature will prevent you from doing what the other nature wants you to do.

Galatians 5:16 gives the requirement for the new nature to be in control of your life. What is that requirement?

_____

Tomorrow you will learn more about what it means to "walk by the Spirit." Start memorizing Galatians 5:16. It's one of your memory verses for this week.

Week 4: Two Natures—
Part One: The New You

Day 2: You Belong to Your Choice

Read Romans 8:10-11; Galatians 2:20; Colossians 2:9-10.

You began yesterday to learn Galatians 5:16—about your new nature. Write as much of that verse as you can remember.

_____

_____

Who controls your new nature according to Galatians 5:16?

_____

We are talking about the whole person when we talk about a person's spirit. We mean his thoughts, his actions, his attitudes, and his desires. Your spirit has been controlled by your old nature (flesh) since you were born. You have been a slave to your old nature. This was done to honor yourself.

But notice that the word Spirit (Galatians 5:16) has a capital *S*. You broke the old nature's control in your life when you become a Christian. You now have a new nature. Christ living in you controls your life through His Holy Spirit. The old nature wants to honor itself. The new nature wants to cause God's love to flow through you.

Find and read Romans 8:10-11. Christ is in you. What is your situation?

_____

You should have written that you are alive. You have the life of Christ now in yourself. You should have written that you have righteousness. You are now right with God. Christ lives in you and controls you.

Don't think your new nature is an "it." You are given the name in Galatians 2:20 of the one who is your new nature. What is that name?

_____

Finish this sentence from that verse. "I have been crucified with Christ..." Christ _____ in me!

That is a wonderful thought. And you live through faith in the Son of God. You can remember the word *faith* in this way:

F orsaking
A ll
I
T rust
H im!

What do you think Galatians 2:20 means when it says that you are supposed to live by faith in the Son of God?

_____

_____

_____

Did you use any of these words in your answer?

surrender   give up   yield   Lord   Master   control

It is your own decision that Christ can control your life. You must fully give yourself to Him. You must decide to let Him be your Lord and Master. You live your choice when you decide to let Christ have control. You become Christ's and not your own.

Remember your hand? Your thumb is one. This helps you remember _____. You should remember the number _____ when you see your forefinger (index finger). What two things are you now learning about? _____ .

Your two natures are discussed in one of the first two verses you memorized. Do you still remember 2 Corinthians 5:17 about the "old" and "new"? Write that verse here.

_____

_____

_____

Write here the parts you know about the hand.

The thumb: _____

The forefinger (index finger): _____

The palm: _____

_____

Colossians 2:9-10 talks about Christ living in us as our new nature. Read those verses. Decide what His living in you really means.

_____ A. If Christ lives in you, so does all the fullness of God.

_____ B. If Christ lives in you, so does the power of God.

_____ C. Both of the above.

Jesus Christ is your new nature. He has come to live in you. He brought the Holy Spirit to be in you. All the power of God himself has been put in you. Christ does not bring the power. He Himself is the power. He has not come to cause you to fail. He has come to cause you to know that God's power can help you be successful in your Christian life.

Remember today in your life that you belong to your choice. Choose the new nature of Christ today. See how He can use your serving and giving. Pray right now. Give Him control of your life today for His purposes.

Answers:
The thumb: 1 Body
The forefinger: 2 natures
The palm: Christ living in me, controlling everything.

Week 4: Two Natures—
Part One: The New You

Day 3: Under Christ's Control

Read Colossians 3:1-7.

Understand once again that Christ lives in you. He Himself is the new nature you have been given. You may often want to ask Christ to vie you something like love, power, and gentleness. He does not give you these things. He is these things. He is in you!

He will let you love, power, and gentleness show through your life if you let Him control your life. He does not give you His skills. He gives you Himself! A good example is that He did not give you a glass of water. He gives you the water well. He has given you the place the water came from. Instead of giving you things you want, He gives you the place those things came from. That is Jesus Christ Himself.

The characteristics (personality) of Christ (your new nature) are shown clearly in your second memory verses this week: Galatians 5:22-23. Have you already made a card and started to memorize them?

Nine things about Christ's personality are listed in Galatians 5:22-23. They are the "fruit of the Spirit". Write each one on the lines that follow.

_____

_____

_____

_____

Your other memory verse for this week also says something about the Spirit. Can you write Galatians 5:16 on these lines?

_____

_____

In Colossians 3:1-7 the apostle Paul says more about your new nature. Read these verses now.

Then read Colossians 2:12-13. How does Colossians 2:12 help you understand the idea "raised with the Messiah" that Paul used in Colossians 3:1?

_____

_____

Remember: Your baptism does not give you your new nature. You already have Christ living in you. Your baptism is a picture of what has happened to you. Did you write something like this on the lines above? *My old life had been buried with Christ, and I am raised to a new life with Christ.*

Now focus on Colossians 3:3. Look at the verses you read yesterday. Some were from Romans. Some were from Colossians. One was from Galatians. Which verse is most like Colossians 3:3?

_____

Did you write *Galatians 2:20*? Do you agree that this verse means almost the same as Colossians 3:3?

Paul said three times in Colossians 3:1-3 that you must make personal choices as a Christian. What choices are you supposed to make?

Verse 1: _____

Verse 2: _____

Verse 3: _____

Think about what you can learn from these verses. Decide what promise you can make for your life today. Pray about your decision for today. Write it on the lines.

_____

_____

_____

_____

As a Christian you might want to use your new nature to do things you think are good things. No, you do not use Christ. Christ uses you. You make the decision to let Christ have control of your spirit, your mind, your emotions, and your body.

The commands in Colossians 3:1,2,5 show your part in the work of your new nature: "seek what is above"; "set your mind on what is above"; "put to death what belongs to your earthly nature".

Your focus should be on Christ. Then He is able to let His love work through you to use your skills (gifts) where He wants to use them! That is a wonderful way to live!

Week 4: Two Natures—
Part One: The New You

Day 4: Christ Within

Read 2 Corinthians 4:6-10; 5:14-18.

The following two words are important for Christians. They are about your new nature.

CONTROLLER (The Holy Spirit controls us.)

CONTAINER (We are filled with the Holy Spirit.)

Read 2 Corinthians 5:14-18.

In 2 Corinthians 5:14 the Bible uses the word *compels*. Another Bible translation uses *controls*. Who should the *controller* of your life be?

_____

Second Corinthians 5:14-15 says that Christ's love compels us. What causes Christ's love to become the controller of our lives?

_____

_____

Did you write something like this? *Christ died for me; therefore, my old self is dead. I now let Christ's love control me.*

Saying 2 Corinthians 5:17 should be easy for you now. Try to say it without stopping. Then write it in these spaces.

_____

_____

_____

One person wrote 2 Corinthians 5:17 this way: *Anyone, no matter who he is, has a new life when he lives in Christ. What used to be there is gone. Everything is now new.*

Second Corinthians 4:6-10 also talks about your new nature. Read these verses now. Which verse uses the example of a container (clay jar)? Verse _____ According to verse 7, what is inside the container?

_____

You will have success in your Christian life because there is treasure in the container. This is because Christ is in the container (you). Second Corinthians 4:6-10 use four comparisons to explain about your success in Christian living. Write them here.

We are	But we are not
_____	_____
_____	_____
_____	_____
_____	_____

Here are the answers from the *Holman Christian Standard Bible*®. Other Bibles use different words that have the same meaning.

We are	But we are not
pressured in every way	crushed
perplexed	in despair
persecuted	abandoned
struck down	destroyed

There's no doubt about it. Becoming a Christian is something that gives you a new nature. You can now let Christ's love control you. You are a container for a new life—Christ's life in you.

You are supposed to let that life control you. You are not supposed to live for yourself. Instead, you live for Christ. You give Him the freedom to use you.

Second Corinthians 4:7 compares you to a clay jar. The clay jar was used in Bible times to hold valuable things. The clay jar itself was not expensive. It became valuable because of what was inside it. You are not a clay jar. You are a person. God does not take your personality away or say you are worthless. Christ, living in you, makes you more valuable to God.

Yesterday you started learning Galatians 5:22-23. It lists the fruit that Christ's Spirit will cause to happen in you. Can you write the nine parts of the fruit of the Spirit?

_____ _____ _____

_____ _____ _____

_____ _____ _____

Read 2 Corinthians 4:6 one more time. Jesus Christ's life in you shows you God's nature. Many people have tried to understand God without letting Him into their lives. They always fail to understand. Only people who have the new nature from Christ can understand God.

Remember that some of your friends may think you have become a "religious fanatic" (crazy from religion). It is impossible for your friends who are not saved to understand the things you experience.

Prayer is fellowship that happens between you and the Father in heaven. This happens because Christ lives in you. As you share things with Him, that is prayer. It is a natural activity for a Christian. Don't make it hard. Just know that prayer is sharing with God. Take time now to pray and keep thinking about this idea.

Week 4: Two Natures—
Part One: The New You

Day 5: Let Christ Be Lord

Read Galatians 5:22-25; Romans 8:26-28.

An apple tree gives apples. An apple tree cannot give peaches. It is by nature an apple tree.

Your new nature also shows fruit. This fruit is listed in a verse you should know by now. Write it on thee lines.

_____

_____

_____

_____

(Galatians 5:22-23)

Check Galatians 5:22-23 in your Bible to be sure it is correct. Notice that the fruit is not what you do. It is what you are. The fruit describes things about your character, not your actions.

Which one of the nine things is impossible for you to do without God?

_____

Which one do you feel you need the most? Underline it in the verse above.

Do you believe Christ can become all of these things in you? Sure He can. New Christians often wonder how they can be sure they are saved. The answer to that question is based on a fact: You have given you life to a God you can trust. He promised to forgive your sins if you asked Him. You asked Him. He did it.

Now that He has kept His promise, you can be sure He will also work in your life. You should now know that some of the fruit of the Spirit—things you cannot copy or do yourself—are now showing in your life. You can be sure that Christ is living in you when you see these things.

Now find and read Romans 8:26-28. Look at verse 26. Do you have to tell Christ that you are weak with a specific thing? Why or Why not?

_____

_____

Never let yourself use an old, worn-out excuse, "I don't pray much because I don't know how I should pray." Christ's Spirit in you can communicate your thoughts and feelings in silent prayer. Other Bible translations say that the Spirit prays for us "in groans that words cannot express" and "with sounds that cannot be put into words" .

Romans 8:27 gives us more support for what verse 26 says. Write the same word two times to finish this paraphrase of Romans 8:27.

_____, Who searches human hearts, can understand what the Spirit means because the Spirit prays only according to the will of _____ .

Romans 8:28 tells the result of your new nature controlling your life. Mark which sentence is closest to being right.

_____ Everything becomes good for people who love God.

_____ God makes everything become good for people who love Him.

You should have marked the second sentence. God doesn't just let things happen. He takes active control of your life as you let Him have control through Christ.

By now you should know well the parts of the hand. Can you fill in the blanks to show what you have learned?

1 _____

2 _____

3 Aspects of Salvation

4 Sources of Authority

5 & 5 Principle

The palm: _____

_____

As you wrote *1 Body*, did you remember your two memory verses? Try saying them now: Romans 12:4-5 and 1 Corinthians 12:18.

As you wrote *2 Natures*, did you remember two more verses? Say Galatians 5:16 and Galatians 5:22-23.

There is a decision you must make because you are a Christian. It is to let Jesus be Lord in your life or not. You must make this decision every day, every hour.

His nature shows the fruit of the Spirit in you when you let Him take control of your life. You do not have to struggle to become like Jesus. You let Him be Jesus Christ living in you, controlling everything. What a wonderful life!

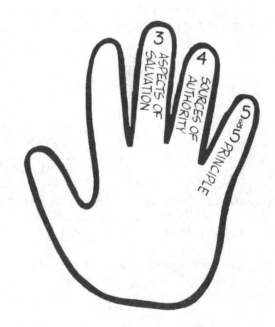

Week 5: Two Natures—
Part Two: The Old You

Day 1: Dethrone the King of Sin

Read Romans 6:12-18.

"That is only human nature." How many times have you heard people say that as an excuse for something a person did wrong?

You know this excuse does not work for you. Christ does not permit people to live following the human nature. He Himself is your new nature. He changes your attitudes and your actions every day.

Your human nature is not gone. It is still there the same as before you became a Christian. Read what Romans 6:12-18 has to say about your nature.

These verses talk about the power sin has to rule your life. We see in verse 12 that we have a choice to let sin have control. Then we must accept what happens.

In verse 17 we learned we used to be _____

Who is King Sin in your life? The way to learn who this is to look at the letter in the middle of the word SIN. Sin is an "I" problem. King Sin controls my life when I choose what I want. I let sin have power to control my body. (See Romans 6:12.) The parts of my body are used for sinful things (Romans 6:13).

As a Christian you belong to what you choose—Jesus Christ or sin. If you decide to let Him control you, Christ will cause the fruit of the Spirit to be present in your life. You become a slave or a servant to King Sin if you decide to let sin control you (it should really be called "King I"). You can expect bad things to happen to you because you disobey God when King Sin controls.

Your old nature is your human nature. It is the nature of sin in you. It was not destroyed when you became a Christian. But, for the first time in your life, sin was not in control. The only time sin has the power to control your life is when you decide to let sin control. You belong to your choice.

Check to make sure you understand.

Who is the new nature in you? _____

Who is the old nature in you? _____

Who decides which one will be in control? _____

Your first answer should be *Christ*. Your second answer might be like any of these:

Myself   *My human nature*   *My sinful self*

King Sin   *King "I"*

And who decides who will be in your control? You do.

Notice the words in Romans 6:12-13: "Therefore do not let sin reign in your mortal body, so that you obey its desires. And do not offer any parts of it to sin as weapons for unrighteousness. But as those who are alive from the dead, offer yourselves to God, and all the parts of yourselves to God as weapons for righteousness."

You must not let any part of yourself be ruled by King Sin. You must let every part of your body be controlled by Christ, who lives in you and controls everything.

What will happen to any part of you that sin has control over? That part of your body will experience sinful use.

What will happen to your body when you give every part to God?

_____

_____

Do you understand how Romans 6:12-13 helps us understand the sentence "You belong to your choice"? Your next Scripture memory assignment also is taken from Romans 6:12-13. This is the longest memory work you have had. It should be becoming easier to memorize God's Word.

Do you remember a verse that tells one of the best ways to prevent sin from ruling your life? It was your first verse to memorize in the *Survival Kit*. Write it here.

_____

_____

_____
(Psalm 119:11)

Check in your Bible and be sure you remember it correctly.

Look again at Romans 6:14-18. Remember that King Sin is not in control of your life. He is not dead. Read these verses. Do you think your old nature will lead you into sin as much now as before you became a Christian?

_____

I hope your answer is *no*. What do you think it means in Romans 6:18 to say that being right with God has power over you now?

_____

_____

One word that appears more than once in these verses might help your answer. What is that word? _____

The meaning is clear. You may choose to obey the sinful self, your old nature. Or you choose to obey Christ, your new nature. You become a slave to the one you decide to obey.

Galatians 5:16 is another way to say almost the same thing. Try to write that verse here.

_____

_____

Week 5: Two Natures—
Part Two: The Old You

Day 2: No Reformation

Read Romans 7:15, 18-21; Galatians 5:19-21,24-25.

One of the hardest things for a new Christian to understand is that your old nature cannot be reformed (changed to improve). You are always frustrated when you try to live in the old nature and show the fruit of the new nature.

Romans 7:15,18-21 shows a Christian who tries to do this. Read those verses. Write in your own words about that struggle.

_____

_____

Did you write something like this?
> *"I want to do good ... but I can't do it."*
> *"I don't want to do bad things ... but I do them."*

Here is a question for you to think about during your Quiet Time. How do you feel your life is like the verses you just read and wrote about?

_____

_____

Now you should find it easy to answer this question. Do you think that Christ gave you new life so that you would be stuck in struggles like the verses in Romans 7:15,18-21?

Yes ❒   No ❒

No, it doesn't make sense that Christ would do that. But it happens because your old nature cannot be reformed. Your old nature is still doing the same things it did before you became a Christian.

Galatians 5:22-23 lists the fruit of the new nature. Write those memory verses here.

_____

_____

_____

_____

_____

Now read Galatians 5:19-21. List the fruit of the old nature.

_____

_____

_____

_____

Count the things in Galatians 5:19-21 that you personally did before you became a Christian.

Write the number here. _____

Next, count how many you have experienced since you have become a Christian.

Write the number here. _____

What does this tell you about yourself?

_____

_____

_____

Many Christians trust their old nature too much. A Christian thinks that giving his life to Christ takes away everything that might make him stray. Christians forget that the old nature can never be reformed.

It's a little like alcoholism. Some alcoholics think they can control themselves. They take a drink. This leads them back into alcoholism. Other alcoholics don't trust themselves. They avoid anything or any place that might tempt them to start drinking again. They know that the temptation might lead them to stray.

Why do we, in your opinion, so easily trust the old nature after we become Christians?

_____

Maybe you wrote that we don't think about sin seriously enough. Maybe that sin uses our trust to take control over us again. Sometimes it requires some hard times in your Christian life to help you realize you cannot ever trust your old self again. *Self, I, sin*—all of these are words for the old nature. It is never going to change. The old nature will always cause the same ugly things in our lives.

That is the reason it is important to remember that you belong to your choice.

Finish today's Bible reading with Galatians 5:24-25. These verses should remind you of Romans 6:12-13, which you started memorizing yesterday. Write here as much of that memory verse as you can remember.

_____

_____

_____

Week 5: Two Natures—
Part Two: The Old You

Day 3: Civil War Within

Read Romans 7:22-25; 8:5-9.

Would you believe that a civil war can happen in your life as a Christian? A war happens when your new nature and your old nature struggle against each other.

Read Romans 7:22-25. This struggle in these verses is caused by a Christian who has not made a clear decision to let Christ be the Lord (controller) in his life.

Romans 7:23 mentions something that happens because of war—being captured. Romans 7:24 shows a terrible situation. A long time ago people invented a terrible way to cause a person to suffer. They would tie a dead body to a person. He would have to carry the dead body with him on his back if he tried to escape.

Paul asked a question in verse 24 that shows he might have been thinking about this horrible situation. What is that question?

_____

"Who can set me free from my sinful old self?" Paul asked. Romans 7:25 gives the name and the title of the one who can free you from this war in yourself.

Write both the name and title here.

Name: _____ Title: _____

Why is the title important in causing the war between your two natures to end?

_____

_____

_____

Jesus Christ must control your life if He is really your Lord. You must follow His lordship. You must refuse to obey your old nature.

Some versions of the Bible use "the old man" and " the new man" while some newer translations use "the old nature" and "the new nature" or "the old self" and "the new self" when describing the war in our bodies.

Look at Colossians 3:8-10a. This is your second memory verse for this week. Notice that the verses you are supposed to memorize end with the first part of verse 10, after "and have put on the new self". Don't postpone starting to work on these verses. It is another long one like Romans 6:12-13. But you can learn both verses this week if you really try.

Other ways to say "the old nature" are "carnal" and "flesh". Remember what these verses mean when you read Romans 8:5-6. These verses show the difference in two kinds of life you can experience as a Christian. One is the life of a Christian that has let the old nature be in control. The other is the life of a Christian that has let the new nature in Christ be in control.

Finish this chart to show the differences according to Romans 8:5-6.

	The Old Nature	The New Nature
Mind-set (v. 5)		
Results (v. 6)		

Romans 8:7-8 makes four negative sentences about a Christian who has not let Christ fully control his life. Finish the sentences about that kind of Christian.

He is _____ toward God.

He does not _____

He cannot _____

He cannot _____

Have you made any decisions about your own life as you have studied Romans 8:5-8? What decisions have you made?

_____

_____

Romans 8:9 tells you that the Christian has the Spirit of God living in him. This means the Holy Spirit is inside him permanently. Is there any time you cannot live with Christ controlling your life? Try to explain your answer here.

_____

_____

_____

You might think it is hard to write on paper your answers to the last two questions. **Remember:** You can pray about them through the Holy Spirit if you cannot put your thoughts into words. Think about the last two questions during your Quiet Time today.

Answers:
He is hostile (fighting against or is an enemy) to God.
He does not submit himself to God.
He is unable to obey God's law.
He cannot please God.

Week 5: Two Natures—
Part Two: The Old You

Day 4: Victory Through Surrender

Read Ephesians 4:22-24; Matthew 5:21-22,27-28; Philippians 4:7-8; Romans 8:37-39.

Today's Bible reading looks long, but there are not many verses. The verses come from several different books of the New Testament.

Begin by reading Ephesians 4:22-4.

These verses should remind you of Colossians 3:8-10. You began memorizing that yesterday. Try now to write it on these lines.

_____

_____

_____

_____

_____

The apostle Paul talked in both Colossians 3:8 and Ephesians 4:22 about a decision that a Christian has to make. The decision is to put away the old person. The point is like a person who has on the same clothes for a long time. He decides to take them off and put them away. He doesn't want them anymore. They are not valuable to the owner. The old clothes will not be worn again.

This decision in a Christian life—to put away the old nature—stops the civil war in you. The old nature is still there. It is alive. But the old nature has no power. You decided to put it away. Your decision to permanently follow Jesus Christ allows His full power to be active in you.

Colossians 3:8-10 lists many things about the old nature. What thing from the old nature do you want to put aside the most?

_____

Paul talked in Ephesians 4:23 about the _____ being renewed. The Lord Jesus Himself also talked about the mind. Read what Jesus said in Matthew 5:21-22,27-28. Jesus said that everything you do begins _____ .

Did you write *in your mind* or *with a thought*?

How can a Christian experience a new mind? Paul gave us good advice in Philippians 4:7-8. Read the verses. Write them here.

_____

_____

_____

_____

One of the best things to use to fill your mind is the Word of God. Do you remember the two verses about gifts and about one body and its service? Write those verses here.

_____

_____

_____

(1 Peter 4:10)

_____

_____

_____

(2 Corinthians 9:7)

How about Colossians 3:8-10? This is one of your memory verses for this week. Try again to write it from memory.

_____

_____

_____

_____

_____

Read Romans 8:37. Find what Christ will give you when you make Him Lord and Master of your life. _____

What will you be? _____

Did you write *victory* and *more than victorious*?

Romans 8:38-39 continues the same idea. It says nothing can cause you to become separated from God's love through Jesus Christ your Lord.

Pay attention to verse 38. It says not even death can separate you from Christ. You might feel that situations in life are your biggest problem as you try to live following the new nature. Christ can have victory over all situations. The only thing you have to do is to ask Him to take control of the situation. That is the purpose of prayer. Why not ask Christ to take control of your life situations today?

Week 5: Two Natures—
Part Two: The Old You

Day 5: One Decision

Read Romans 6:1-11.

The apostle Paul didn't like excuses. Read Romans 6:1-2 to find out if Paul would accept any excuse for living with the old nature in control. What question did Paul ask in verse 2?

_____

Paul spoke in Romans 6:3-5 of baptism as your public confession that something has changed in your life. What does that confession show to other people?

_____

_____

You show in baptism that your old sinful self is dead. You now have a new life in Christ. What does Romans 6:6-7 say happened to cause the old nature to have no more power over your life?

_____

Paul said that your old nature was crucified with Christ (nailed to the cross). How are you to live as a Christian if your old nature has been nailed to the cross? The answer is in Romans 6:8-11.

_____

Here is one way to say it, "When sin looks for me, it finds out that I am dead. But when God looks for me, He find me alive through Jesus Christ." Does this make sense to you?

Paul continued to write some words that you have memorized. Can you write Romans 6:12-13 on these lines from memory?

_____

_____

_____

_____

_____

Check and see how well you have memorized these verses.

Think about your life as a Christian. Do you sometimes brag to your friends about your Christian life? Afterwards, do temper, lust, bitterness, or frustration appear in your life? Because of these internal conflicts, do you begin to feel that maybe you are not really a Christian? Maybe you feel embarrassed. You try to pretend to live like a good Christian. You know people are watching you. You know it is a "pretend" Christian life you are living.

Many other people have tried to do that. They pretended to live as victorious Christians. They did not show people their real situation. They became busy. They did activities for the Lord. They thought activities for the Lord or the church would cause them to have a holy life. Then they slowly understood that they were only pretending to live good Christian lives. There was no peace or victory inside. They felt like hypocrites. They slowly quit all Christian activities because they felt discouraged. They became defeated Christians.

You now know the truth that these other people were not taught in time. Every Christian has a new nature and an old nature. You cannot pretend to live the Christian life. Christ, who is the new nature, wants your old nature to live a new, changed life. You must always choose to fight against your old nature.

The Christian life does not mean trying to be like Jesus. That is impossible. Instead, you let Jesus Christ, God's Son, become the controlling King in your life. You give Him the right to lead your thoughts and control your actions. You decide now and for the future that He came into your life to become your Lord. He is the One to whom you belong.

Living as a Christian means not only doing some things. It is mostly holding inside yourself another Person. As you read your Bible now and in the future, you will understand this more and more. Christ is in you. He is your new nature. You decide to let Him be the leader of your life— your words, your habits, your thoughts—everything. He becomes the Ruler in your life. He will shine through your life because He has given you spiritual skills called gifts. You will always know that the life you have every day is not yours. It is His!

Think about it this way. You decide you want to become a football player. You don't have all the strength and skill you need. But you try. You run until you are exhausted. You throw the ball with all of your strength. The best you can do is not enough. You know that you have failed.

Then, on the sidelines, a man walks to you. He introduces himself. He is on of the greatest football players in the world. He offers to do a strange thing for you. He tells you he can take the strength from his body and put it in your body. He also says he will give you everything he knows about football to put in your mind.

You accept his offer to give you strength and knowledge. You go back on the football field again. You are throwing perfectly. You are running faster than you thought possible. Your mind thinks about the game. You know all the things you are supposed to do. The people are cheering for you! You are playing the game like a professional. But in your heart you know the reason you are playing like this. You have the power and strength of a famous football player inside you. Other people may cheer. You know the real reason is because another man gave you the skill to do it.

Christ does exactly that for you in your Christian life. He gives you the power, the strength, and the knowledge to do the things you cannot do alone. He does these things for the rest of your life. You belong to your choice. Let Him be the Lord in your life— today, tomorrow, and forever. Christ promises you great victory!

Week 6: Three Aspects of Salvation—Part One: Its Beginning and End

Day 1: Three Aspects of One Event

Read Philippians 1:3-11.

When you became a Christian, maybe you thought praying to accept Jesus would give you everything Christ had to give you. Well, you were right.

You experienced forgiveness when you prayed and Christ came to live in you. You also received some rights from God at that same time. The rights are yours now. You also were given an inheritance. The inheritance is yours for the future.

Salvation is experience in three stages: past, present, and future. The apostle Paul knew about this. He explained it to his friends in Philippi?. Read what Paul wrote in Philippians 1:3-11.

What did Paul do every time he thought about his Christian friends in Philippi? (See v. 3).

_____

Paul thanked God for the Philippian Christians. What emotion did he always feel when he prayed? (See v. 4.)

_____

What did Paul thank God for as he prayed with joy about his Christian friends in Philippi? (See v. 5.)

_____

Paul had special feelings for the Philippian people because they had told other people about the gospel and had been Paul's helpers. How did he describe those feelings? (See v. 7.)

_____

Paul expressed his feelings that the Philippian people were dear (special) to him. What love did Paul compare his feelings to? (See v. 8)

_____

Paul had a special love for the Philippian Christians. This love was like the love of Jesus Christ for each of us. This is the reason he wanted to be sure they understood the three aspects of salvation. No other verse in the Bible explains this more clearly than Philippians 1:6.

Be sure to notice the times Paul stressed as you complete the exercise on the next page.

Fill in the blanks based on Philippians 1:6: *"I am sure of this..."*

The Beginning Point	Happens Through Time	The Final Event
_____	_____	_____
_____	_____	_____
_____	_____	_____
Freed from the **penalty** of sin	Freed from the **power** of sin	Freed from the **presence** of sin
Cleansed by Christ's **blood**	Liberated by Christ **living in you**	Given your inheritance by Christ's **second coming**

Did you write *"that He who started a good work in you"* on the lines in the left column? Did you write *"will carry it on to completion"* in the middle column? Did you write *"until the day of Christ Jesus"* in the right column?

Do you understand how this simple chart gives you a better picture of your salvation? Are you surprised to learn that Philippians 1:6 is your next Scripture memory assignment?

Look at the chart again. Notice that when you accepted Jesus Christ as your Lord and Savior you were only beginning your salvation! There is much more to come. You know you belong to God. Do you also know all Christ has for you? You already have your salvation; but, knowing what that means lets you enjoy it more deeply.

What have you found that your salvation does for you in your everyday life? Read Philippians 1:9-11 to help you think of ways your salvation helps you.

Write your answer during your Quiet Time.

_____

_____

_____

_____

_____

Week 6: Three Aspects of Salvation
Part One: Its Beginning and End

Day 2: Salvation Past

Read Ephesians 2:3-6,8-9,12-13,17-19.

All the Bible verses in today's lesson are about salvation past. That is the time in your life when you prayed, asking Christ to enter your life as Lord and Saviour.

What did God do when you gave Him your life? Ephesians 2:5 tells us two things God did. Write them here.

1. _____

2. _____

Did you write *He made me alive with the Messiah* and *I am saved by grace*?

Verse 6 gives two more explanations of what God did when you became saved. Write them here.

3. _____

4. _____

God raised us from death. He has given us a place with Christ in the heavens. Why is it important to notice the words *we* and *us* in verses 5-6? Ephesians 2:19 should help you understand.

The things you studied in Week 2 of your *Survival Kit* will help you. What do you remember when you look at the thumb on your hand? Who is it that causes us to be "1 Body"? What are you supposed to remember when you look at the palm of the hand?

_____

"Christ, living in me, controlling everything" is important when you remember what your forefinger (index finger) reminds you of. What is it?

_____

Your thumb should remind you that we are "1 Body" in Christ. Your forefinger (index finger) should remind you that we have "2 Natures". What does your middle finger remind you about?

_____

You should have written *3 Aspects of Salvation*. This is the subject you are now studying. What Bible verse tells you about salvation past, present, and future more clearly than any other? Write it here.

_____

_____

(Philippians 1:6)

Return now to your study in Ephesians 2. According to verses 8-9, what did you do to deserve God's forgiveness through Christ?

_____

I hope you understand Ephesians 2:8-9 so clearly that you wrote *Nothing* on that blank line. Now read Ephesians 2:12-13.

What does it mean when it says: "But now in Christ Jesus, you who were far away have been brought near by the blood of the Messiah" (Ephesian 2:13)?

_____

Ephesians 2:17-18 makes it clear. He proclaimed the good news of peace to us who were far away from Him.

You can go to God the Father through the Holy Spirit.

Now read again Ephesians 2:3,5,12,17. What was the situation when Christ saved us from sin through His blood? How many of these things were true about your life?

_____

_____

_____

_____

Here are a few of the things you could have written. Beside each one put the number of the verse.

Sinful   (v. _____)

Dead   (v. _____)

Far Away   (v. _____)

No Hope   (v. _____)

Without God   (v. _____)

Without Christ (v. _____)

Answers:
Sinful (v. 3)
Dead (v. 5)
Far away (v. 17)
No hope (v. 12)
Without God (v. 12)
Without Christ (v. 12)

For your entire life, you will never stop being surprised about the things Christ did for you. You prayed and asked Him to come into your life at that time. He took you out of a world where self controls all decisions and pleasures. He instantly forgave all the sin and wrong things you had done. He made you clean as if you had never sinned. He put His own life inside of you. He made you belong to His kingdom. He caused you to become free from worry about facing God for judgment.

These things are finished. Nothing can take away your new life in Christ. You belong to Him forever.

Week 6: Three Aspects of Salvation Part One: Its Beginning and End

Day 3: Baptism of the Spirit

Read Romans 8:9-11; Ephesians 1:12-13; 1 John 4:12-16.

Salvation past … a specific time that happened in your salvation experience. You prayed. You confessed your sin of living and controlling things yourself. You asked Jesus Christ to forgive you of all the sin in your life. You invited Jesus to become your Lord.

Today's Bible verses teach us that at that specific time important things happened. Read Romans 8:9-11. Notice how the names in the *Trinity* (God, Jesus Christ, and the Holy Spirit) are used in these verses. How many of the names can you find and write?

_____

_____

_____

_____

Notice that all these names for Trinity are used interchangeably. Romans 8:9 talks about all three Persons of the Trinity. So does verse 11.

Now read these verses again. Notice the words "lives in you." You received the fullness of the Trinity when you gave your life to Christ.

The point is this: the Trinity cannot be divided. You also received the Holy Spirit from God when you Received Christ. He came to live in you at that specific time.

The apostle Paul used Ephesians 1:11-13 as an interesting example from his culture. In that time some people used a seal or stamp with his own personal sign—like a seal from a Notary Public. The person would push it into hot wax or clay to mark things he owned. Sometimes the seal (or stamp) was on a ring a person wore on his finger.

Read Ephesians 1:11-13.

What is God's mark on you? Write it here.

_____

The Holy Spirit is God's seal on you. The seal proves you are His. Did you notice these verses use the titles of the Trinity several times? Circle how many persons of the Trinity are mentioned in Ephesians 1:11-13.

1   2   3

Your second memory verse for this week also comes from Ephesians. You studied part of it yesterday. Look now at Ephesians 2:8-10. Study the chart that outlines your new verse. Finish the chart by writing the words from Ephesians 2:8-10.

How are you saved?	Why?	How are you *not* saved?	Why not?

As you wrote the phrases, did you notice that Ephesians 2:8-10 discusses the three things about salvation? The column named *"How are you saved?"* talks about salvation past. That is the specific time when by grace through faith you received God's gift, Jesus Christ. You became a new part of God's work. The column named *"Why?"* talks about salvation present. This is how Christ living in you now causes you to do the good works that God made you for.

Have you already memorized another verse that speaks of salvation past and that talks about both salvation present and salvation future? Can you say Philippians 1:6 now? (Be sure to check yourself by looking in your Bible.)

Now read carefully 1 John 4:12-16.

How many persons of the Trinity are mentioned in these verses? Circle the correct number.

1 2 3

Three persons are mentioned. How many live or dwell in us?

1 2 3

How many have been given or sent to us? Circle the correct number.

1 2 3

Did you find all three? The **Son** has been sent as your Savior and the Savior of the world. The **Spirit** has been given to you. And **God** Himself dwells in you. That is a wonderful, true teaching from the Bible. You are a container for the Father, the Son, and the Holy Spirit. You never have to ask for Christ or the Holy Spirit again. God is already in your life!

That is a finished thing. Your salvation will never have to be repeated. Hebrews 13:5 promised He will never leave you nor forsake you.

Week 6: Three Aspects of Salvation
Part One: Its Beginning and End

Day 4: Salvation Future

Read Ephesians 1:13-14; 1 Peter 1:3-9,13; 1 Thessalonians 4:15-18.

Salvation future … the final experience in your salvation.

Yesterday Ephesians 1:13 taught that you received the Holy Spirit at the exact time you gave your life to Christ. Read that verse again now. Also read verse 14. Do you see the important information that verse 14 adds? The Holy Spirit that you already have is a "down payment" for much more that God has reserved for your inheritance.

The King James Version of Ephesians 1:14 uses the word *earnest*. You put earnest money as a deposit on a house when you buy it. That money is a promise to pay the full price when the house becomes yours.

This is a strong promise about salvation future! The down payment (earnest money) has already been paid. You have the Holy Spirit. Some day Christ will take you to be with Him. He will receive as His own the people He has bought with His blood. He put a deposit on you through the Holy Spirit. There will be a time when you will receive everything related to salvation.

Read carefully 1 Peter 1:3-5. Do these verses talk about salvation past or about salvation future?

_____ A. Salvation past   _____ C. Both past and future

_____ B. Salvation present   _____ D. Neither past nor future

The right answer is that these verses are about both—that which Christ has already done for you (salvation past) and that part of your salvation that will happen in the future. When you read your Bible now and in the future, look for verses that discuss the three things about salvation.

Read 1 Peter 1:6-9. What things about salvation do you see in these three verses?

_____ A. Salvation past   _____ C. Both past and future

_____ B. Salvation present   _____ D. Neither past nor future

Do you agree that *D* is the best answer? First Peter 1:6-9 talks about your faith in Jesus Christ. You have never seen Jesus with your eyes. This is salvation past. It also discusses problems you experience now that help prove your faith is real. This is salvation present. And it also talks about a future day when the testing of your faith will cause praise and glory and honor. This is salvation future.

Verses 7 and 13 tell you the exact time when you will experience everything about salvation. When is that time?

_____

You will experience everything about salvation when Jesus comes to take you with Him, His second coming. Read 1 Thessalonians 4:15-18 to get a better idea about that day of Jesus' coming. Be sure to thank God in your Quiet Time for His promise about salvation future.

How is your daily Quiet Time? It has been about 40 days since you started using the *Survival Kit*. How many days you think you have had a good time of Bible study and prayer? _____

Are you faithful to memorize Bible verses? **Remember:** One important reason for learning verses is so you will know what the Bible says when you need to know. Here are 10 verses you should have learned in the first weeks of your *Survival Kit*. Draw a line to match them with the topic you studied each week. Try to say the verse as you do this.

Christ in You   Psalm 119:11,
                                       Romans 6:12-13
Church Life   Romans 12:4-5
                                       1 Corinthians 12:18
Church Service   2 Corinthians 5:17
                                       2 Corinthians 9:7
Two Natures: The Old You   Galatians 5:16
                                       Galatians 5:22-23
Two Natures: The New You   Colossians 3:8-10
                                       1 Peter 4:10

Check your *Survival Kit* lessons to be sure you matched each one correctly. But it is more important to check your Bible to see if you remembered all of the verses correctly.

Are you having problems remembering the basic points that you have studied in the *Survival Kit*? You should remember them **1-2-3!** Write them here as you would write them on the hand.

1. _____

2. _____

3. _____

> **Answers:**
> 1. Body
> 2. Nature
> 3. Aspects of Salvation

Can you remember the verse that best explains salvation past, salvation present, and salvation future? Try saying Philippians 1:6.

One more thing needs to be studied about the future salvation the Lord has for you. What is your inheritance?

Tomorrow we will study about that. Remember: There is more to come. You are promised that it is reserved for you. You will get it when Jesus Christ comes to take you to Himself.

The future part of salvation is so important that Christians a long time ago called it "the blessed hope." Both life and death can be important for Christians: Our King is coming!

Week 6: Three Aspects of Salvation Part One: Its Beginning and End

Day 5: Free from the Old Nature

Read Romans 5:12; 6:23; 1 Corinthians 15:50-57; 2 Corinthians 5:1-9.

Salvation future! What will salvation give you that you do not have now. You will not have it until Christ comes again. The Bible gives the answer. The Bible calls it your inheritance.

Read Romans 5:12 and Romans 6:23. What two short, awful words are in these verses? _____ and _____

What is the relationship between sin and death?

_____

Will you ever be finished with your old nature, the sin nature? Yes! Death will happen to every person because of sins. Only people who are alive when Jesus comes again will not be hurt by death. But there will be a time in the future when you become free from the sin nature. It will be finished forever.

Read 1 Corinthians 15:50-57. Write the numbers of the verses that answer the questions below.

A. What verse tells you about future salvation will happen at a specific time?

A. Verse_____

B. What verse connects death with sin?

B. Verse_____

C. What verse says you cannot have the kingdom of God with the old nature in you?

C. Verse_____

D. What verses promise you eternal life because the old nature will be taken away?

D. Verses _____

E. What verse promises that this is the work of Jesus Christ—not the result of you doing good things?

E. Verse_____

> **Answers:**
> (A: 51-52, B: 55-56, C: 50, D. 53-54, E: 5)

Do you remember some Bible verses that clearly say you are not saved because you do good things? Try to say Ephesians 2:8-10 from memory.

Now think about the teaching in 2 Corinthians 5:1-9. Verse 1 describes our bodies as "temporary earthly dwellings." Verses 2-4 describe us as "groaning" in our body. What, in your opinion, is the best reason for our groaning?

_____ A. Christians have a hard time in this life.

_____ B. Christians are afraid of dying.

_____ C. Christians want to be free from the old nature.

Verses 2 and 4 make the right answer clear. Paul said in verse 8 that he preferred to be free of his body with the sin nature. Then he could be at home with the Lord.

Now look carefully at 2 Corinthians 5:5. It should remind you of Ephesians: 1:13-14, which you have studied twice this week. What same things do you notice in these two passages?

_____

You see once again that you already have the Holy Spirit as a promise or down payment of the future inheritance God has for you. Write in your own words what you know about salvation past and salvation future.

_____

_____

_____

Did you remember that both are things that happen at specific times? Jesus' death on the cross already saved you from the punishment for sin. Your inheritance at the time of salvation future will mean throwing away the old nature. Write here the verse you have learned about putting off the old nature.

_____

_____

_____

_____

_____

(Colossians 3:8-10)

Now, are you ready to review the hand again? You should be able to write in four blank spots. (Check yourself by page 4.)

The palm _____

The thumb_____

The forefinger (index finger)_____

The middle finger _____

Week 7: Three Aspects of Salvation
Part Two: The Daily Process

Day 1: Salvation Present

Read Romans 5:6-11.

Remember the three aspects of salvation.

Salvation past ...   Christ's blood causes you to become forgiven from sin forever and not to experience the punishment from sin.

Salvation future ...   Christ's coming back will cause you to become free from the presence of sin.

Salvation present ...   Christ living in you causes you to now be free from the power of sin.

A man in prison was told the governor of the state had given him a full pardon (forgiveness) for the things he had done wrong. The man in prison was very happy. He asked to be let out of prison. The prison warden said, "No, we cannot let a man like you out of prison!"

What value is forgiveness if you don't have freedom now?

_____

Christ has given you, right now, freedom from sin's power. Study Romans 5:6-9.

What thing about salvation do these verses talk about?

_____

In the middle of verse 9, the point changes from salvation past to salvation future.

Romans 5:6-8 explains God's great love that sent Christ to die for sinners like us. This explanation of salvation past continues in verse 9. It says, "since we have now been declared righteous by His blood" (Romans 5:9). The point changes to salvation future in the middle of that verse when it says "we will be saved through Him from wrath" (anger).

Romans 5:10 also begins by talking about salvation past. We were enemies of God. But we were saved from the punishment of sin by the death of Christ.

What other thing about salvation does the verse mention?

_____

Who causes our salvation present? (See Romans 5:10.)

_____

Can you use verse 10 to finish this sentence? By Christ's death, I have received salvation _____. Now, through Christ's _____, I daily receive salvation _____.

Through Christ's life, you daily receive salvation present. Romans 5:10 should remind you about Galatians 2:20 (a verse you studied a few weeks ago about your new nature). What same teachings do you find in both verses?

_____

_____

Did you write something like this? *Romans 5:10 says I am saved by Christ's life. Galatians 2:20 says Christ lives in me. I now live by faith in Him.*

Read Romans 5:11.

Salvation present means you can give thanks to God. This means that you can be happy and jump for joy. Can you list three things in your personal life that Christ has brought you? These things cause you to give thanks to God.

1. _____

2. _____

3. _____

Romans 5:10 is an important verse for understanding salvation present—whatever you wrote, whatever causes you to be happy in your Christian life. Never forget Who brings these joys into your life now. The reason you enjoy salvation present is because of Christ. He is living in you, controlling everything.

It should not surprise you that Romans 5:10 is your next memory verse.

Romans 5:10 uses the word *reconciled*. Do you know what *reconciled* means? Being reconciled means _____

_____

Being brought back to God is something we cannot do ourselves. You have learned a verse that explains being brought back to God is the gift of God Himself. He makes us new people in Christ Jesus.

Here is the same chart you saw when you started learning Ephesians 2:8-10. Can you write the parts of the memory verse in the right places on the chart?

How are you saved?	Why?	How are you *not* saved?	Why not?

Look back at the lesson in Week 6, Day 3 to see how you did filling in the chart. Look at your Bible to see if you remembered your Scripture verses correctly.

Week 7: Three Aspects of Salvation
Part Two: The Daily Process

Day 2: Saved by His Life

Read Hebrews 2:14-15,18; 4:14-16; 1 Corinthians 10:13.

Saved by His Life—Salvation now because Jesus Christ lives in you. He gives you His power to cause you to become free from sin.

Does Jesus really understand your needs? Your weaknesses? Your temptations? Today's Scripture passages can help you realize He does understand all of these things.

Read Hebrews 4:14-16. These verses show Jesus in a way the Jewish people could easily understand. There was a high priest in the Jewish religion. He went to God and gave sacrifices so that sin could be forgiven. What kind of priest is Jesus? Where did He go?

_____

_____

Jesus is our great High Priest. He has gone to God. (See v. 14.) How does Christ feel about the temptations to sin that we experience? (See v. 15.) Why does He feel that way about your temptations?

_____

_____

Jesus understands your weaknesses. Why? Because He Himself was tempted in every way we are tempted. Notice the important difference between Jesus and every other person who has lived: He did not sin.

The Bible tells us in Hebrews 4:16 that we are able to do something. Jesus has saved us and understands our temptations. What are we able to do?

_____

_____

Go with complete trust to the place of God's loving favor. Ask God for the strength you need to resist temptation. Read Hebrews 2:14-15,18 after you pray. What did Jesus do in verse 15 to help Him understand you perfectly?

_____

Jesus became a man. He had the same kind of flesh and blood you have. To what length did Jesus go to understand everything a person must experience on this earth?

_____

The words in Hebrews 2:14 gives the clear answer. He became flesh and blood and endured everything you must endure. He also shared the experience of death. There is nothing in your life Jesus did not also experience. He faced the same things you face.

Jesus' experience caused two wonderful things to happen. One is in Hebrews 2:14. The other is in Hebrews 2:15. Finish these two sentences:

1. Jesus destroyed the power of the devil, who has the _____ of death.

2. Jesus freed us from the _____ of death.

Neither the power of death nor the fear of death can control you. You have Christ living in you. You are saved by Christ's life.

Hebrews 2:18 makes it clear that Jesus experienced many different things as a person. Read that verse. How can you be sure Jesus fully understands your temptations and sufferings?

_____

Because Jesus was tempted as we are and suffered as we do, He understands us and He is able to help us when we are tempted. Write here one temptation or one problem you are facing today.

_____

Do you believe Jesus Christ understands your situation?

Yes ❏   **No** ❏

Do you believe Jesus Christ can help in your situation?

Yes ❏   **No** ❏

Yes, He understands. Yes, He can help. Yes, He lives with you in all of your life.

Do you remember a verse that reminds us that with the Holy Spirit's help you do not have to do what the human nature wants? Write that verse here.

_____

_____

(Galatians 5:16)

Do you remember a verse that lists the fruit Christ will cause in your life because of salvation present that He gives you? Write it here.

_____

_____

_____

_____

(Galatians 5:22-23)

Many verses in the Bible are so important that you should never forget them. One of the 10 most important ones is 1 Corinthians 10:13. Read it now. Today's Bible study should cause this verse to have a deep meaning for you. Take 5 minutes to think about it. Think about every part of it with what you have learned from the verses in Hebrews.

Understands that salvation present is yours today. Your victory depends on Christ living in you. Christ has experienced everything you now experience. You are saved by His life!

Week 7: Three Aspects of Salvation
Part Two: The Daily Process

Day 3: Victory in the Spirit

Read Ephesians 5:18; John 7:37-39.

Christ living in you brings victory to every part of your life. Jesus was faced with everything you face. He did not sin. He will not permit you to be tempted more than you can resist. He will always vie you a way to resist temptation and avoid sin.

He protects you. He gives you everything you need. Read Ephesians 5:18. This verse talks about a drunk person. Too much wine has changed his personality. All who meet him know that something is not normal about him. You are told in a like way to be filled with the Spirit. There is a change in your personality when you are filled with the Spirit. Other people who meet you will know that something is different about you. Being filled with the Spirit changes who you are and what you do just like drinking too much wine changes who you are and what you do.

It is important to know things about a Greek word in Ephesians 5:18. The Greek word is translated *be filled*.

1. It is a word that means always do it; always be filled.

2. It is a command word—an order for us to obey.

It is obvious that this is not an optional part of the Christian life. You are commanded to always be filled with the Holy Spirit.

In Ephesians 5:18 the apostle Paul compared drinking wine to being filled with the Holy Spirit. Jesus compared things in the same way in John 7:37-39. Read these verses now.

Who will give a drink? (See John 7:37.) _____

What is the drink Jesus was talking about? (See John 7:39.)

_____

Jesus said it was the Holy Spirit. Paul said the same in Ephesians 5:18.

Look in John 7:38. What happens when a person has the Holy Spirit? _____

_____

Rivers of living water will flow in your life. That is a beautiful picture.

Does this remind you about your spiritual gifts that are ways for Christ's love to flow through you? Can you write your two memory verses about spiritual gifts?

_____

_____

_____

(1 Peter 4:10)

_____

_____

_____

(2 Corinthians 9:7)

What Jesus said in John 7:38 should also remind you of one thing you have learned today about the words translated *be filled* in Ephesians 5:18. Can you figure out how they mean the same thing?

_____

Do rivers of living water always flow? Yes, they do. Ephesians 5:18 tells us to always be filled with the Spirit. This part of salvation is a daily process. It should remind you that you are saved by the death of Christ and also by the _____ of Christ.

Can you write Romans 5:10 here? It is the memory verse that explains this important idea.

_____

_____

_____

Your other memory verse for this week should not surprise you. It is the verse you were told about yesterday. This verse is so important you should never forget it. Do you remember where to find this verse? Look at yesterday's lesson to find it. Then write it here.

_____

_____

_____

_____

_____

_____

(1 Corinthians 10:13)

Now look again at John 7:37. What do you have to experience to decide to go to Jesus for a drink?

_____

Salvation now is promised by Jesus Christ. He wants to give you His Spirit in a way that you will always have it. The only thing you need to do is to go to Jesus when you become thirsty. He will give you what you need.

Are you thirsty?
Come to Jesus Christ and
be satisfied.

LIVING WATER

Week 7: Three Aspects of Salvation
Part Two: The Daily Process

Day 4: Working out what God is Working in

Read Philippians 2:5-13; Hebrews 13:20-21.

Jesus Christ, the Son of God, understands everything you face in your daily life. He experienced it all for your benefit.

One of the clearest explanations of this is in Philippians 2:5-8. Read those verses now.. It may help you to know that verse 6 could be stated as: "Christ Jesus was in the form of God but did not think of equality with God as something He must hold on to." In verse 7, Jesus became like two things that show He was willing to experience anything you experience. What two words show this?

_____ _____

Did you write *servant* or *slave* in one of these blanks? Did you write *man* or *human* in the other blank?

What word in verse 8 shows Jesus was willing to do everything required to share your experience? _____

What did God do because Jesus was willing to die? Read Philippians 2:9-11. Write in your own words what God has done.

_____

_____

_____

Here is one way to say it: "God has made Jesus higher than all and will cause all to confess that fact." Exactly what will every tongue say according to verse 11?

_____

Now read Philippians 2:12-13. Do these verses seem to be strange or in the wrong place? They came right after God has caused every tongue to confess that Jesus Christ is Lord. You are told that God has lifted Christ high above everything. Every knee must bow before Him. You are told to keep on working "with fear and trembling" that you will not please Him. That seems a strange thing to say.

Can you please God by working for your salvation past? No, you cannot. You have already memorized a verse that tells you this is impossible. Write Ephesians 2:8-10 here.

_____

_____

_____

_____

Can you work for your salvation future? No, you have also memorized a verse that tells you how you will be saved. Write Romans 5:10 here.

_____

_____

_____

This means that the command in Philippians 2:12 to work to show you have been saved must mean your salvation present (now)—that every day living with Christ where He fills and leads.

Notice the two kinds of work in Philippians 2:12-13. You are supposed to work to show your salvation. God is working in you to cause you to please Him. Salvation present means God's Spirit always being in your personality so His gifts can flow through you.

Read again Philippians 2:12. Why are you supposed to have "fear and trembling"? You are not supposed to be afraid that God is angry and will punish you. No. It must mean something else. It means you fear missing God's blessing in your life. You fear failing to permit God's Spirit to control you will cause you to displease Him.

The clearest explanation about the three things of salvation is in Philippians 1:6. Write that verse here:

_____

_____

_____

_____

Now read Hebrews 13:20-21. What will God teach you to do? What will God make you able to do ?

_____

_____

Whom does God use to cause it to become possible for you to do His will? _____

God is working in your life now through the power from Jesus Christ that lives in you.

What is God doing in your life at this moment? Think about it during your Quiet Time. Write your thought on these lines.

_____

_____

_____

_____

_____

_____

Week 7: Three Aspects of Salvation
Part Two: The Daily Process

Day 4: Salvation Is Rescue

Read Colossians 1:9-14.

It should be clear to you that God has done, is doing, and will do the action of salvation in your life. Salvation begins at a specific time: This is when you confess your sin and accept Christ as Lord. Salvation continues as a daily process. You become free from sin's power through Christ's living in you and controlling every thing. In the future Christ will free you from the sin nature in your life.

Read Colossians 1:9-14. What verses explain salvation past? What verses explain salvation present? What verse explains salvation future?

Colossians 1:10-11   **Colossians 1:12**   **Colossians 1:13-14**

Salvation past: _____

Salvation present: _____

Salvation future: _____

(You should have written the reference in this order: 13-14; 12; 10-11.)

Colossians 1:9 says Paul was praying for a special kind of knowledge. What was Paul praying for people to know?

_____

_____

God wants you to know what He wants you to do (see Colossians 1:9) He wants you to understand how His salvation is experienced in three ways—past, present, future. He wants you to know that your salvation past is sure because of Christ's death on the cross. He wants you to feel that you have no doubt about your salvation present (now). Christ's life gives you strength to resist temptation to sin. What Bible verse helps you know this? Write 1 Corinthians 10:13.

_____

_____

_____

_____

_____

_____

One important idea has been saved until our last study about the three aspects of salvation. Exactly what is *salvation*?

Imagine you are standing beside a lake. You see a man in the middle of the water. He cannot stay afloat. He will soon die if someone doesn't save him. What will kill him? Water. He will drown in water. He must be taken out of the water to be saved.

The word *salvation* means you need to be saved from something that will kill you. What will kill you? Colossians 1:14 tells you that sin will kill you. You are drowning in sin. You must be taken out of the sin to be saved.

Do you remember the meaning for sin in your *Survival Kit*? Sin means taking the "I" and making it the king of your life. Sin is an "I" problem.

You are in a dangerous situation when you live a self-owned, self-controlled, self-decided life. Colossians 1:13 says that people who live for themselves are in a life of darkness. This kind of life will destroy a person.

Salvation is leaving the self's life and getting the Christ's life. Salvation is not only a way to die. It is not only a life insurance policy for eternal life. It is much, much more.

Salvation is God saving you from a self-directed life. He took you out of that situation at a specific time. He makes it possible for you to live with Christ directing your life as a daily process. He will in the future make you free forever from the possibility of a self-life. That is salvation.

Be sure you understand this point. You need to know what salvation means for the rest of your life with Christ. You have been "called out" of a world where everyone lives for himself. You have been put into a body of people, the Body of Christ. All in this Body have the desire for Christ to be their Lord and their King. They are together. They have chosen to be Christ-controlled rather than self-controlled. Salvation means becoming controlled by Christ.

Read again Colossians 1:9-14. Read these verses slowly. Salvation is the changing of "boss" from you to Christ as we grow in Him.

Remember that all of this is possible because Christ died for you on the cross. He took your past life into His own sinless body. He accepted the punishment that should have been for you. He caused you to become free. Then He rose from the dead to fill you with His own Spirit. He has a purpose for your life. His plan for you life is to use you to channel His love. That is a wonderful life!

Week 8: Four Sources of Authority
Part One: Three Weak Sources

Day 1: Four Sources of Authority

Read Colossians 2:1-4,8,20-23.

"I want to see somebody with authority around here!"

How many times have you heard or said words like that? Sometimes every person likes to work with the boss. Sometimes every person needs to talk to a person who has authority.

All religions have one of four kinds of authority. Only one kind is right. There are many people around the world trying to find important things in life. They are following a weak kind of authority.

This week you will study three dangerous kinds of authority. Your friends may try to use one kind of authority when you try to talk with them about your faith. You will concentrate next week on the one true kind of authority you can trust.

Study the following chart that discusses the four kinds of authority. You will notice that there are four words above the chart. Write the word in the blank that fits the best meaning.

Experience Knowledge	Scripture Tradition
Sources inside man himself	*Sources outside of man*
_____	_____
Man decides what is true by thinking about what is good or bad, right or wrong.	Man follows things that were important to other people who lived before.
_____	_____
Man decides what is true by his feelings and what he sees, hears, and touches.	God shows what is true in His Book; He gives information to people.

> You should have written the words like this:
>
> Experience — Knowledge
> Scriptur[e] — Tradition

Paul, the apostle, knew a lot about weak kinds of authority. He traveled as a missionary. He met many people who depended on the wrong kinds of authority. They did not depend on the right kind of authority. Some books Paul wrote in the New Testament are for helping people know the right kind of authority.

Read Colossians 2:1-4. Paul said in verse 2 that he wanted them to be rich. What kind of riches did he mean?

_____

Paul told the Colossian Christians he wanted them to understand. In verse 3 Paul told them that in Christ Himself they would have:

_____

Why did Paul want them to have the riches of wisdom and understanding? Verse 4 tells you.

_____

_____

You need to know what Paul wrote in Colossians 2:8 to make sure nobody deceives you with wrong kinds of authority. Read it now.

How may wrong kinds of authority did Paul talk about in Colossians 2:8? Write here words that match each one.

Knowledge: _____

Traditions: _____

Experiences: _____

Did you notice that these three kinds of authority are mentioned in verse 8 in the same order that they are listed above? "Philosophy" is knowledge. "Empty deceit" is tradition. The idea of "elemental forces of the world" is experiences.

What did Paul mean when he said your mind could be taken captive by these wrong kinds of authority?

_____

_____

Have you met a person whose mind was changed by some false idea so strongly that he or she would not pay attention to what you were trying to say? Your Bible memory verse for this week explains how a person can be changed by false ideas.

Look at 1 Corinthians 2:14. Tomorrow you will study this verse more deeply. Begin to memorize it now.

Now read Colossians 2:20-23. What did Paul say to convince us to not live following only man-made rules? Look at the beginning of verse 20.

_____

"You have died with the Messiah," Paul said. That is the reason you should not follow man-made rules. They are regulations from man, "commands and doctrines of men" (Colossians 2:22-23).

God gave you your mind (knowledge); He expects you to use it. God gave you experiences. They may be important. Some things never change. Some traditions are worth keeping. But knowledge, experience, or tradition should not become your authority for faith.

Week 8: Four Sources of Authority
Part One: Three Weak Sources

Day 2: Intellect! Reason! Logic!

Read Mark 12:18-25; 1 Corinthians 1:18-25; 2:7-14.

Many people let their intellect (what they know) make final decisions. If it seems logical to me, I will do it! Doing this makes you become your own God. People are bigheaded to think their intelligence can make decisions about truth and false things, good and bad, right and wrong.

All of history reminds us that people make bad decisions. Kingdoms appear and disappear because of bad decisions. There are still people who say, "I can't understand how a good God could …" or "It doesn't make sense to believe God would …"

Jesus Himself had to talk with people who thought this way. Read Mark 12:18-25. The Sadducees were an important group in the Jewish religion when Jesus was alive. Verse 18 says the Sadducees did not believe in resurrection. The Sadducees told Jesus a long story to support not believing in resurrection after death. What was their story from?

   ___ The Bible   ___ Their own ideas

What did Jesus say about the Sadducees' thinking? (See Mark 12:24.)

Jesus said they were _____, because they did not

know the _____ or the _____.

The Sadducees were wrong. They did not understand the Holy Scriptures or the power of God. Do you think the Sadducees were really trying to learn when they came to talk to Jesus?

          Yes ❑   No ❑

What kind of authority did the Sadducees have for their religious beliefs?

_____

The apostle Paul had to help people who made intellect (what they know) the authority for their religious ideas. (Read 1 Corinthians 1:18-25.) There is a word in verse 20 that describes the Sadducees who were talking to Jesus: *foolish.* They were not trying to learn because they thought they had all the answers. Thinking you have all the answers does not help anyone learn. Paul also said in verse 20 that God has made foolish all the wisdom of the world.

Paul analyzed the way two large groups of people in his lifetime used the wisdom of the world: The Jews were looking for signs (something special to see). The Greek people were looking for the answer in wisdom. But Paul preached that Christ died on the cross to save them from their sins. Those words were hard for the Jews to hear. The Greek people thought it was foolish.

Christ is the power and wisdom of God to those who are chosen to be saved from the punishment of sin. God's plan looked foolish to men, but it is wiser than the best plans of men. God's plan which may look weak is stronger than the strongest plans of men.

The Christian faith is not opposite to being intelligent. The apostle Paul was one of the best-educated and most-intelligent men at that time. Read 1 Corinthians 2:7-8 to learn what kind of wisdom Paul taught. He said that if people on earth had understood God's wisdom, then they would not have done what terrible thing?

_____

No, Paul did not say that people have too much wisdom; they don't have enough. They would not have put Christ on a cross to die if they had God's wisdom. Now read 1 Corinthians 2:9-11 to learn why people of the world did not understand who Jesus was and why He came. Verse 11 tells us that the only person who understands God's thoughts is the

_____ .

The Holy Spirit is the only one who understands God's thoughts. How can people understand them? Verse 12-13 tells us how. Write these verses in your own words.

_____

_____

_____

Did you write something like this? *God gave us the Holy Spirit to teach us about God's ways.*

Read 1 Corinthians 2:14. Why is it impossible for a person to find God through his own ideas?

_____

The person who is not saved does not have the Holy Spirit and cannot understand God. Does this mean you cannot convince a lost person to become saved through intellect?

Yes ❐   **No** ❐

Yes, a person who depends on what he knows for authority cannot be convinced to become saved. You must ask God to use His Holy Spirit to convict and prepare the person to become saved.

You should have felt comfortable with 1 Corinthians 2:14 when you read it today. Can you write it from memory?

_____

_____

_____

_____

Week 8: Four Sources of Authority
Part One: Three Weak Sources

Day 3: Experiences! Visions! Feelings!

Read Deuteronomy 13:1-4; Colossians 2:18-19.

People have started religions since the beginning of the world based on the experiences they have had. They have called other people to share these experiences after letting experience be the authority for their religion. A person who has not had the same experiences must seek to experience them. Or the other people will think he is not good in that religion.

Trying to find the truth in an experience is a serious problem. How do you know that what a person is saying is true or not if he tells you that he has had a vision from God? Authority that depends on experience is a dangerous thing. That is the reason God shows Himself to people in a better way. He has given us a written record of what is true. You can compare all experiences to the Bible to know if they are really from God.

You can find a good example of this in Deuteronomy (the fifth book in the Bible). Read Deuteronomy 13:1-4. Which one is a better test of truth in a person who is a prophet or a dreamer?

_____ A. If the prophecy or dream happens.

_____ B. If the prophet or dreamer tries to convince you to leave the one true God.

The teaching is clear. It doesn't matter if someone can show you signs and miracles. Even if his prophecies come true, you must not pay attention to him if he causes you to focus less on God. Deuteronomy 13:2-3 explains why people who make experience their religious authority seem to be convincing. What reason does that verse give?

_____

God might use a prophet, a dreamer, or a miracle-worker to test your love for Him. But He will not let the testing become too hard for you. Last week you learned a verse that promises God will give you a way to escape. Can you write 1 Corinthians 10:13 from memory?

_____

_____

_____

_____

_____

Experience is only one of _____ different kinds of authority in religious things. Do you remember seeing "4 Sources of Authority" on the picture of the hand? How much do you remember about other things you have studied in your *Survival Kit*? Try to finish the outline on the next page.

1 _____, which is _____

_____

2 _____, which are _____

_____

3 _____, which are _____

_____

4 _____, which are _____

_____

Your second memory passage for this week talks about one of the three weak kinds of authority. Tomorrow you will study 1 Peter 1:18-19a. Start learning it now. (Note that the memory part ends in verse 19 with the word *Christ*.)

Think again about the problems that people who depend on experience cause. Read Colossians 2:18-19. What specific problem was the apostle Paul writing about?

_____

_____

It seems that some of the people in the Colossians church had experienced visions. As a result they were trying to make all the Christians join them in worship of angels and in other false religious activities. Verse 19 says that these people are not a part of the

_____.

Verse 19 also says our growth in the church comes from _____

_____ .

The apostle Paul made a strong statement about people who depend on experience as their authority. He said they are not a part of Christ. Christ is the Head. We Christians make up His Body, the Church. Experiences often do not help people become strong together in the church. Experience often causes divisions. People who have experience sometimes think that people who do not have experience are not as good. But Christ did not stress experience. He gives you His own life. This is what causes growth from God.

Be sensitive to people who encourage you to look for experiences. It can be a blessing to all of the people when God gives you a special time of fellowship. But be careful when you begin to look for the experience more than the time of fellowship with God. You might be following a false kind of authority.

Week 8: Four Sources of Authority
Part One: Three Weak Sources

Day 4: Tradition!

Read Matthew 15:1-9; 1 Peter 1:18-19.

"It's a tradition! We've always done it this way! We must not change!"

How do traditions happen? Someone in the past decided that an event, a special service, or a special teaching should happen again and again. The event was important and special for that person. It had to be continued. It must not be forgotten.

Often, however, the meaning of the special event becomes lost. It becomes a regular event that nobody knows what it means. It does not help people. It does not cause people to make deep commitments. Tradition becomes a heavy burden that prevents people from understanding the real meaning of the event if it was done in a new and different way.

Read Matthew 15:1-9. Why were the religious leaders of Jesus' time criticizing His disciples?

_____

_____

_____

Jesus' disciples did not follow tradition., They didn't wash their hands the exact right way before eating bread. Jesus said the religious leaders were breaking more important laws. Which one of the Ten commandments did Jesus say the religious leaders were breaking?

_____

The religious leaders were braking the Commandment, "Honor your father and mother." Jesus said in Matthew 15:6 that two kinds of religious authority are conflicting with each other. Which two?

_____ against _____

You must make a clear choice when Scripture goes against tradition. Write in your own words what Jesus told the leaders in Matthew 15:8-9.

_____

_____

Some people say good things but do not do them with their hearts. They follow people's ideas and opinions and not God's Word. The verses you began to memorize yesterday has an important point for this kind of person. Try to write it here.

_____

_____

_____

(1 Peter 1:18-19)

Can tradition help people become saved? The verses in Matthew that you study today tell us why tradition cannot help people become saved. What is that reason?

_____

_____

Did you write that tradition is often only empty words and actions. It is often not from the heart. Sometimes traditions can conflict with God's Word. First Peter 1:18-19 says that people can be saved by what? And what were you saved from?

_____

_____

Are there people you know who are stuck in religious tradition or habits? People who are missing the true blessing in life? People who can be saved by Christ's blood from the punishment of sin and worthless tradition? Carefully write the names of a few people you know who are stuck in tradition. Then pray for them by name in your Quiet Time.

_____   _____   _____

_____   _____   _____

Have you found one of the great benefits of memorizing Bible verses? You don't have to limit your Quiet Time to sitting down to read your Bible. You can meditate on the Bible verses at any time when you have them recorded in your heart and mind.

Check your progress in memorizing the verses you have been given. Mark only the verses you can say without looking now.

_____ Psalm 119:11		_____ Romans 6:12-13
_____ 2 Corinthians 5:17		_____ Colossians 3:8-10
_____ Romans 12:4-5		_____ Philippians 1:6
_____ 1 Corinthians 12:18		_____ Ephesians 2:8-10
_____ 1 Peter 4:10		_____ Romans 5:10
_____ 2 Corinthians 9:7		_____ 1 Corinthians 10:13
_____ Galatians 5:16		_____ 1 Corinthians 2:14
_____ Galatians 5:22-23		_____ 1 Peter 1:18-19

MEMORIZING THESE VERSES IS IMPORTANT BECAUSE SCRIPTURE IS YOUR AUTHORITY AS A CHRISTIAN!

Week 8: Four Sources of Authority
Part One: Three Weak Sources

Day 5: Intellect! Experiences! Tradition!

Read 1 Timothy 1:3-7; 6:20-21; 2 Timothy 2:15-19.

Intellect, experiences, tradition… Separately or together, these three kinds of religious authority can never become more than human ideas without God. All are based on human ideas. All of these give no eternal benefits.

It is not true to say that all religions lead to the same God. A person who says this has never studied all religions. Some religions do not admit that there is a might God.

As a new Christian you will see many different kinds of religious teachings. Many serious and kind people will share their opinions with you about religion. Analyze each opinion carefully.

Are they based on intellect (what people know)? *A person's mind cannot be the final judge of truth.*

Are they based on someone's experience? *People's activities cannot become the final kind of authority.*

Are they based on tradition? *People's past knowledge and experience cannot be trusted more than what he has now.*

Read 1 Timothy 1:3-7. Verse 4 tells us what man-made teaching does to people. What do man-made ideas do to people?

_____

Stories that are not true do nothing to help you as a Christian. What does teaching from God do? (See v. 5)

_____

_____

First Timothy 1:5 talks about a true love that comes from a pure heart. What was wrong with the false teachers according to verse 7?

_____

To become a teacher of the law in the time of the New Testament meant you had great honor. Do you still see people today who want to get honor and glory for themselves by teaching from weak kinds of authority? Read 1 Timothy 6:20-21. What did Paul tell Timothy to do with the true things God had given him?

_____

How should Timothy act toward false teachers if he kept safe the true teaching?

_____

Paul wanted Timothy to turn away from foolish talk and not to argue with false teachers. Second Timothy 2:15-19 has more instructions from Paul to Timothy. Which kind of authority is talked about in verse 15?

_____

Hymenaeus and Philetus turned away from the words of truth, the Scriptures, to another kind of authority. Read verses 16-18. Which kind of authority do you think they followed?

_____

It seems that intellect was the kind of authority these two men followed. (See vv. 18-19.) Do you think they were successful in their teaching? Think about the answer both ways. Explain why.

Yes: _____

No: _____

Yes, these false teachers had made the faith of some people become weak. No, the truth of God cannot be changed.

This is the only week you have used your *Survival Kit* to study the four kinds of authority. But you have been learning since the beginning of *Survival Kit* that Scripture is your authority as a Christian. What Bible verse tells you what Christ has done for you by His life and death? Write here Romans 5:10.

_____

_____

_____

_____

Now it is time to look back at what we have learned. What are the things you have learned in the past eight weeks?

Remember: Look at your hand. You should be able to write these:

The palm _____

The thumb _____

The forefinger (index finger) _____

The middle finger _____

The ring finger _____

How did you do?

Week 9: Four Sources of Authority
Part Two: One Strong Source

Day 1: Holy Scripture,
The Only Authority

Read 2 Timothy 1:1-2,5; 3:14-17.

Four sources of authority … but only one can be trusted! The apostle Paul knew which authority could be trusted. Read 2 Timothy 3:14-17 again.

Focus on verse 15. How long had Timothy been studying the Scriptures?

_____

Timothy had studied the Scriptures since he was a child, Timothy knew the Scriptures were able to give him what?

_____

This wisdom leads to what?

_____

What other writings in the world can lead you to salvation through faith in Christ Jesus? None!

Focus now on 2 Timothy 3:14. What did Paul tell Timothy to continue to do?

_____

_____

What is the difference in learning something and firmly believing something?

_____

Firm belief happens when the people who teach you also show you these things in their own lives. Verse 14 says that Timothy knew who his teachers were.

Do you know who Timothy's teachers were? Find three of them in 2 Timothy 1:1-2,5. Write their names and relationships to Timothy.

_____, who was Timothy's _____ .

_____, who was Timothy's _____ .

_____, who was Timothy's _____ .

Lois was Timothy's grandmother, and Eunice was Timothy's mother. What relationship did you list for Paul? In verse 3 Paul called Timothy his son. He was using *son* as an example.

It seems that Timothy's father was dead or was not present in his life. He was not there when Timothy was growing up. Paul had become like Timothy's spiritual father. This is the reason Paul called him "my dearly loved son."

What do these verses tell you about your example and your influence on the children and young people around you, both in your family and in your church?

_____

_____

Focus now on 2 Timothy 3:16. Who inspired the Scriptures?

_____

The Bible is profitable (useful) for four things because God inspired it. What are they?

_____   _____

_____   _____

The Scriptures are useful for teaching the truth, rebuking error, correcting faults, and giving instructions for right living. The Scripture will influence your life if you study it. What will you become as you study the Scripture?

_____

_____

Do you really want to become fully qualified and equipped to do every kind of good deed? You know how if you do. You are doing it now if you are faithful in reading the Bible in your everyday Quiet Time, working in your *Survival Kit,* and memorizing your Bible Verses.

Do you still remember your first memory verse in the *Survival Kit?* This verse explains why it is so important to memorize God's Word. Write Psalm 119:11 here.

_____

_____

Second Timothy 3:16 is another verse that tells you the Bible is important. Start memorizing it today! Do you know what that verse means when it says the Scriptures are inspired? *Inspiration* means breathed in. You could say that inspiration means "God-breathed" when you read the sentence (2 Timothy 3:16).

Scripture is God's work. He breathed His truth into men's minds who wrote the books in the Bible. The Bible is truth. It is the only, perfect record of God's truth or people. Some other writings and commentaries may help you understand God's Word. None of them is required for knowing God. It matters whether it is a book, a vision, an experience, or a tradition. These things must be under the authority of the Bible.

Timothy had been studying Scripture since he was a child. You cannot start your own lifetime study sooner than today. Make a prayer promise.

Will you give time to reading God's Holy Scripture for the rest of your life?

Week 9: Four Sources of Authority
Part Two: One Strong Source

Day 2: Scripture Before Experience

Read 2 Peter 1:16-21; Matthew 17:1-5.

You have read many Bible verses that Paul wrote. These verses are in Bible books called Paul's Letters. Paul's letters are followed by another part of the Bible called General Letters. Two books in this part were written by Peter.

Read 2 Peter 1:16-18. Peter talked in these verses about a wonderful event he had witnessed. That event was the *transfiguration* of Jesus Christ. Read these things Peter said about it.

_____ "We were eyewitnesses of His majesty."

_____ "He received honor and glory from God the Father."

_____ "A voice came to Him from the Majestic Glory: 'This is My beloved Son. I take delight in Him'!"

_____ "We heard this voice when it came from heaven."

_____ "We were with Him on the holy mountain."

Now read Matthew 17:1-5. Write the number of the matching verse in Matthew in the blank space in the previous column. Some verses will be used more than once. You will see that Peter's words match what really happened.

> **You should have written verses in this order:**
> 2, 5, 5, 1, 1.

It is clear Peter knew what he was talking about. He stood on the holy mountain. He saw Jesus receive honor from God the Father. He heard God's voice from heaven. Peter said in 2 Peter 1:16 that he knew that the power of the Lord Jesus Christ was not a

_____

No, the event on the mountain was not a man-made story that some people tell. It really happened. Peter was there to see it happen!

Read carefully what Peter said in 2 Peter 1:19-21. Did you notice that he said his experience helped him know that what the prophets said was true? Peter's experience was true. He was there. He was an eyewitness. He believed the Bible. What the prophets said was more true than his own experience. Peter was saying, "The Bible can be trusted more than my own experience. It was written by men who were led by God's Holy Spirit."

Peter said in 2 Peter 1:20-21 two important negative things about the Bible. Write here in your own words what Peter said.

1. _____

2. _____

93

Peter said that the Bible is not made up of man's interpretation of truth. No part was made up because of what man wanted to write. The bible was written because God planned it. God spoke to holy men to write what the Holy Spirit told them to write.

Now write here four kinds of religious authority.

_____   _____

_____   _____

Write an *X* beside the kinds of authority Peter was using when he told what happened with Jesus on the Holy mountain. Write two *Xs* beside the kind of authority Peter said was better.

Your list should look like this:	
KNOWLEDGE	TRADITION
EXPERIENCES X	SCRIPTURE XX

What rule should you have in your life about authority? What should be the most important kind of authority in your life? Pray about this during your Quiet Time. Then write your answer here.

_____

Last week you memorized something Peter said about another kind of religious authority—tradition. Can you write 1 Peter 1:18-19 from memory?

_____

_____

_____

_____

_____

_____

Your second memory verse for this week is 2 Peter 1:20-21. Get an early start by beginning to memorize it now!

Now is also a good time to learn what the word *prophecy* means. A man whose life, words, and writings were controlled by God's Spirit in the Old Testament was called a *prophet*. A *prophet* was a person who spoke God's words. Sometimes these words told about the future. Often they did not tell about the future. A prophet was a man who said whatever God told him to say. A prophet did not say his own words. God gave the words!

A PROPHET IS A "FORTH-TELLER" OF GOD'S WORDS

Week 9: Four Sources of Authority
Part Two: One Strong Source

Day 3: An Amazing Book

Read Micah 5:2, Matthew 2:1-6; 27:13-14,38,57-60; Isaiah 53:5,7,9; John 14:2-3; ;19:1,4,34; 20:25.

The Bible has hundreds of stories about things that had not yet happened when the men wrote about them. The Bible has prophecies about future kingdoms and kings, births and deaths, and stories about the Savior coming into the world in its pages.

For example, read Micah 5:2. Then read Matthew 2:1-6. Where did Micah say the Savior would be born? _____

Where was Jesus born? _____

Micah said in the year 740 B.C. the Savior would be born in Bethlehem. Mary, Jesus' mother, lived in Nazareth. Mary had to travel to Bethlehem because of the Roman government's order. Jesus was born during the time Mary was in Bethlehem. Mary did not know these things would happen when she became pregnant. Read Isaiah 53:5,7,9:

5—He was pierced because of our transgressions (wrongdoing).
5—He was crushed because of our iniquities (sins).
5—He was punished so we would have peace.

5—He was beaten so we would be healed.
7—Man caused Him to suffer. (He was oppressed and afflicted.)
7—He did not open His mouth.
9—They made His grave with the wicked (sinful).
9—He was with the rich at His death.
9—He had done no wrong (No violence.)
9—There was nothing false in His mouth (No deceit).

Read the New Testament verses listed below. Write beside each one the number of the verse above that it matches. Notice that the prophet was correct in telling the facts about Jesus' trial, suffering, crucifixion, death, and burial.

_____ John 19:34	_____ Matthew 27:14
_____ John 20:25	_____ Matthew 27:38
_____ John 19:1	_____ Matthew 27:57-60
_____ Matthew 27:13	_____ John 19:4

Here is how you should have marked these verses from Isaiah:

5—John 19:34	7—Matthew 27:14
5—John 20:25	5—John 19:1
7—Matthew 27:13	9—Matthew 27:38
	9—Matthew 27:57-60
	9—John 19:4

It is so interesting that Isaiah 53 was written hundreds of years before Christ was born. People at that time did not know about using a cross to kill a person. But the words *pierced because of our transgressions* fit the use of the nails on the cross and the sword used by the soldier.

Also notice Isaiah 53:9. How could anyone know that Jesus would have a "grave with the wicked" and yet be buried "with a rich man at his death." Only God's Spirit could tell the prophet these things.

How much have you learned about the Bible? Test yourself by taking the "Twelve Books of the Bible" test in the next column.

Our Lord Jesus Himself once made a prediction about the future. Read it in John 14:2-3. What two things did Jesus prophesy?

1. _____

2. _____

Jesus predicted He would go to make a place for you in heaven and He would come back to take you with Him to that place. Do you have a reason to believe this will really happen in the future? Explain your answer here.

_____

_____

Many Bible prophecies have already happened. This is the reason you can know that the other prophecies will also happen in the future. The Bible is a book full of prophecies. Only God could make every one of them happen exactly as He said. God's Word is a really amazing book.

You should now be feeling more comfortable with the Bible. Your study in *Survival Kit* has not taught you everything you need to know to take this test. Don't feel bad if you do not know all the answers. If you know all the answers, it shows that you have been learning facts about your Bible from other places.

TWELVE BOOKS OF THE BIBLE

Match these twelve book names with explanations given below. (You have studied from all except one of them in your *Survival Kit*.)

Genesis	**Isaiah**	**John**	**Philippians**
Deuteronomy	**Micah**	**Acts**	**1 Peter**
Psalms	**Matthew**	**Romans**	**2 Peter**

Two letters from Paul:

_____

_____

Two letters from Peter:

_____

_____

The beginning of all things:

_____

A book of praise songs:

_____

Two books of prophecy:

_____

_____

Two biographies of Jesus:

_____

_____

The beginnings of the church:

_____

A book of rules:

_____

Week 9: Four Sources of Authority
Part Two: One Strong Source

Day 4: A Forever Place for Wisdom and Righteousness

Read Psalm 19:7-11; 37:29-31; 119:89-91,98-101,130,160; Isaiah 40:6-8; Mark 13:31.

What does the Bible say about itself?_____

_____

Read these two explanations before opening your Bible.

1. You will find many different words that mean the Word of God, the Bible, in the verses you will study today. Some of these words are *law, precepts, testimonies, statutes, commandments, judgements.*

2. The words *Word of God* mean more than just the Bible. They mean anything that God says about Himself. God may say things about Himself through the beauty of the world He has made, the voice of His prophet, or through the history of the world. The *Word of God* means the active revealing (showing) of God's personality. God's personality can be seen in the Scriptures. This is the record of God's activity.

Now read carefully all of the verses listed at the beginning of this page. These verses focus on the things the Bible says about itself. It lasts forever. It is a place to find wisdom. It is a place to find righteousness. Write the correct verse beside each word that it explains:

Forever: _____

Wisdom: _____

Righteousness: _____

Answers:
Forever: Psalm 19:9; 119:89-91,160; Isaiah 40:8; Mark 13:31
Wisdom: Psalm 19:7; 119:98-100,130
Righteousness: Psalm 19:8-9,11; 37:29-31; 119:101

You have also been learning some other Bible verses that have something to say about the Bible. Can you write them from memory here?

_____

_____

_____

_____

(2 Timothy 3:16)

_____

_____

_____

(2 Peter 1:20-21)

Another verse you have learned explains why many people misunderstand the Bible. The Bible was inspired by God's Spirit. It can only be understood by people who have the Spirit of God living in them. Write a verse here that explains this point.

_____

_____

_____

(1 Corinthians 2:14)

Always remember to check yourself when you say or write a Bible verse from memory. Don't memorize the verses the wrong way.

Now look again at Psalm 37:31. Where should God's Word be kept?

_____

It is comforting to know that when God's Word is in your heart, your life will not stray from God's ways.

Here are eight verses you have learned in the past four weeks.

Draw a line to match each of them with the subject you studied the same week. Also try to say each verse from memory.

Three Aspects of Salvation—   —Romans 5:10

Its Beginning and End—   —1 Corinthians 2:14

Three Aspects of Salvation—   —1 Corinthians 10:13

A Daily Process—   —Ephesians 2:8-10

Four Sources of Authority—   —Philippians 1:6

Three Weak Sources of Authority—   —2 Timothy 3:16

Four Sources of Authority—   —1 Peter 1:18-19

One Strong Source of Authority—   —2 Peter 1:20-21

Check your *Survival Kit* to be sure you matched each verse correctly. It is even more important that you check your Bible to be sure you said each verse correctly.

The most helpful part of memorizing Bible verses is to review, review, REVIEW! Review every new verse every day for six weeks. This should help you learn it. You can remember it after that without a lot of pressure. Review the verse once a week after that for six weeks. Then review once a month for all of your life. This is not to much work if it gives you a forever place to get wisdom and righteousness!

Week 9: Four Sources of Authority
Part Two: One Strong Source

Day 5: Four Sources of Authority or One?

Read 1 Corinthians 15:3-7; Acts 18:24,28; Hebrews 5:12-14.

Four kinds of authority, but only one can be trusted. You know which one can be trusted.

Paul also knew which one could be trusted. Read what Paul wrote in 1 Corinthians 15:3-7. Paul said two times what authority he was using to tell of the death, burial, and resurrection of Jesus Christ. What kind of authority was it?

_____

Can you use the same authority Paul used?

Yes ❐   No ❐

Yes, you can use the Scriptures as your authority when you are talking about Christ's life with other people. But, this doesn't just happen to you because you become a Christian. Read in Acts 18:24,28 about a Christian man named Apollos. How do you think Apollos became skilled in his knowledge of the Scriptures?

_____

_____

Do you think it is important for **you** to know the Scriptures the same as Apollos knew them? Is it important for you to fix your schedule and choices so that you can **study the Scriptures** the same as Apollos did? What might have to be changed in your life to give you the time for the lifetime habit of everyday Bible study?

_____

Honestly, are you ready and willing to do the changing right now?

Yes ❐   No ❐

Read Acts 18:28 again. What did Apollos do before he was able to show that Jesus was the Messiah, the Christ?

_____

Would you like to be able to share Christ?

Yes ❐   No ❐

If yes, what can you do to make yourself ready as Apollos did?

_____

Read Hebrews 5:12-14. Some of the people never started the habit of everyday Bible study. What happened to them?

_____

_____

It is awful when people should become teachers but still need someone to teach them the basic things about God's Word. These people are the opposite of Apollos.

Write the names of one or two Christians you know who remind you of Apollos.

_____

_____

Write the one or two who remind you of the Christians in Hebrews 5:12-14.

_____

_____

Think for a minute! Do you think your name might be on some other person's lists? Do you remind people of Apollos, who knew a lot of the Bible? Or do you remind people of the Hebrew Christians who never grew up? Pray about that during your Quiet Time.

There are four kinds of authority, and only one can be trusted.

God gave you a mind to think and learn with. God did not mean for your mind and your knowing things to become the authority in deciding what is right and wrong. Your mind is for God to use to find His leading.

God gives all Christians experiences. You, too, will have experiences. These experiences are not supposed to be the things you follow. Experiences happen because you have a wonderful fellowship with God. Experiences might disappear in the future. Jesus Christ is the same yesterday, today, and tomorrow, Your fellowship with Jesus must not let your experiences with Him become too important.

Some tradition (the same as knowing things and experiences) might begin in God's plan. However, you are stuck in tradition when you do things from empty habit and do not understand why these things are valuable. Only Christ can help you become free. Knowing Christ personally is better than only knowing habits that mean nothing to you.

Finally, you come back to Scripture, the perfect kind of authority. Everything you need to know about faith and life as a Christian is found in the Bible. It makes sense that no part of your life as a Christian should be more important than your personal Bible study with God's Word.

Pastors preach the Scriptures. Teachers teach the Bible. They believe it is the perfect authority. You will benefit from their preaching and teaching. But there is a more important benefit for you to have. It is the benefit from a personal relationship. You have read may Bible verses in the past nine weeks. It hasn't taken a long time each day, has it? Don't break the habit of everyday Bible study when you have finished your Survival Kit. You will soon become like Apollos if you will continue this same time daily for the rest of your life.

You will find people in your church (the Body of Christ) who have special skills to put deep things from the Bible into words. Become friends with these people. They will bless your life But don't forget. Study the Word. Memorize the Word. Meditate on the Word. Christian growth will happen when you study the Bible and pray each day.

Week 10: The 5 & 5 Principle— Five You Can Win By Prayer

Day 1: The 5 & 5 Principle

Read Philippians 4:6; 1 Timothy 2:1,3-4,8.

Look at your left hand. Use the fingers to count five people you know right now who will not permit you to talk about Jesus with them. These people are cold. Maybe they make fun of your life in Christ. You have a strong wish to share your new life with them so they may also enjoy it. But they will not listen to your talk about Jesus Christ.

What can you do? Pray for them!

Look at your right hand. Use those fingers to count five people you know right now who will permit you to talk about Jesus with them. They may not be ready to let Christ control their lives. They are curious about the changes they see in your life.

What can you do? Witness to them!

You will have fewer friends who are not Christians as you grow in your Christian life. People who recently become saved have more friends who are not saved than they will ever have again. It is important for you to do everything you can do now to share Christ with those people.

Your Bible study next week will focus on witnessing. But the power of prayer is more important than witnessing. It can work with people who will and people who will not let you share Christ with them. A Christian once said, "You can do more than pray, after you have prayed. But you can do nothing more than pray—until you have prayed."

Look now at Philippians 4:6. This verse tells us there is one thing we can do instead of worrying. What can you do?

_____

Does the verse put limits on things you can pray about?

_____

As a Christian you can talk to God about everything. What is prayer? Prayer is letting Christ use His power to work where there is a need—in your life or in other people's lives. The answer to your prayer does not depend on your power in prayer. It depends on His power to work and take care of the need. This is the reason praying for people you know who are not Christians is asking Christ to work in their lives no matter what their attitude is about your witnessing.

Read 1 Timothy 2:1. Paul told us in this verse that prayer needs to be made for whom?

_____

Praying for all people may seem to be too much. In 1 Timothy 2:3-4 Paul explained two reasons why God wants us to pray.

1. _____

2. _____

God wants everyone to be saved. He wants everyone to know the truth. You should pay attention to how God wants these things to happen, Paul said in 1 Timothy 2:8 one more thing that God wants. What is it?

_____

The talk about lifting up hands in 1 Timothy 2:8 reminds us that this was the normal way for people to pray in Paul's lifetime. You, too, may stand with your hands lifted up towards heaven. Or, you may kneel, be seated, or even be busy in some regular activity while you are praying.

The position of praying is not important. The habit of praying is important. You have learned by experience that the habit of prayer and the habit of Bible study go together. Do you remember a memory verse telling you that God's Holy Spirit talks to you through the words written in your Bible?

_____

_____

_____

_____

(2 Peter 1:20-21)

Your new verse to learn this week is Philippians 4:6. It is the first one you were asked to read today. Do more than only memorize it. Put it into practice in your life.

Use the chart to become ready to use the 5 & 5 Principle in your life as a Christian. Carefully list in the left column the names of five people who will not permit you to talk with them about Jesus Christ. Prayerfully list in the right column the names of five people who will let you talk with them about new life in Jesus Christ.

These friends will not let me share Jesus Christ with them	These friends are open to my sharing Jesus Christ with them
1. _____	1. _____
2. _____	2. _____
3. _____	3. _____
4. _____	4. _____
5. _____	5. _____

Week 10: The 5 & 5 Principle— Five You Can Win By Prayer

Day 2: A Little Faith is Enough

Read Matthew 17:20; 21:21-22; James 1:5-8; John 6:37.

You have been asked during this time in the Survival Kit to use your hand in two different ways. Yesterday you looked at your fingers. You were asked to think of five people on one hand and then five more people on the other hand. What two groups of people are you supposed to remember on your two hands?

_____

_____

You were asked to remember on your left hand five people who will not let you share Christ with them. You were asked to remember on your right hand five people who will let you share Christ. The first group you can pray for. The second group you can both pray for and witness to. Your hands can remind you how the 5 & 5 Principle works in your life as a Christian.

The other way you have used your hand as a reminder was back in the beginning of the *Survival Kit*. Remember and list the meaning of the numbers 1-2-3-4-5 as they go on your hand to help you remember **five things** you have studied.

1_____

2_____

3_____

4_____

5 & 5 _____

> **You should have written:**
> 1 Body
> 2 Natures
> 3 Aspects of Salvation
> 4 Sources of Authority
> 5 & 5 Principle

If you had any problems remembering these five things, you may need to study again that part of your *Survival Kit*. Read the beginning of your *Survival Kit* again. Which one thing above must work closely together with the others?

_____

103

You have remembered that 1 Body in Christ, the Church, has a special relationship to the other things you have learned . What about the palm of the hand? What does it help you remember? What is more important to your Christian life than any of the other things you have learned?

Christ living in me, controlling all is what you should remember when you look at your palm. What verse reminds you that these things may seem foolish to other people even though they are important to you?

_____

_____

_____

_____

(1 Corinthians 2:14)

Now read Matthew 21:21-22 and James 1:5-8. Do the verses you read cause you to feel discouraged or depressed as you thing about praying for the salvation of your friends? They might. Write here the fear you feel about praying for other people.

_____

_____

Maybe you wrote some words like this: *If my faith isn't strong enough, God will not answer my prayers. Prayer is not for me. I'm honest to admit that I have weak faith.*

Read another Bible verse: John 6:37. Jesus said this about people: "The one who comes to Me, I will never cast out."

Read Matthew 17:20. How much faith do you need to have for Jesus to answer your prayers?

_____

Jesus said that faith as small as a mustard seed is enough.

Do you have enough faith to pray and talk to Jesus about your needs? He has promised that He will not turn away anyone who trusts Him.

Jesus will help you with doubts if you have enough faith to tell Him about them. Don't feel your faith is so weak it will do no good to pray. Prayer is letting Jesus' power work where there is a need—in your life or other people's lives.

Is your faith in Jesus enough to ask Him to use His power to show Himself to your 5 & 5 people? Then, it is enough. The best faith is when a person admits his limits. He leaves everything to Jesus. Don't be afraid you will limit Jesus' power by your faith. Pray.

The only way you will learn about the power of praying in reaching people to become saved is to pray for them. Think today of each of the people on your 5 & 5 list from yesterday. Give them to Jesus one at a time. Pray about a specific thing in each life. Invite Jesus to touch that need with His power. Then wait and see what happens. God has His own time for answering. And answer He will!

Week 10: The 5 & 5 Principle— Five You Can Win By Prayer

Day 3: Three Parts of Prayer

Read Matthew 7:7-11.

The title of today's study should sound familiar (Three Parts of Prayer). You have also learned about three aspects of

_____

They are: _____

_____

The three aspects of salvation are past, present, and future.

These are not the same as the three things we will study about prayer. All of these are part of your present fellowship with God. What memory verse tells you that it will be useful or will profit you to have an everyday fellowship with God by Bible study? Write 2 Timothy 3:16 here.

_____

_____

_____

_____

What memory verse tells you that you can and should have constant communication with God by prayer?

_____

_____

_____

(Philippians 4:6)

Now read Matthew 7:7-8. We often describe praying as talking with God. These verses from Matthew explain praying as three things. You can see three parts of prayer in the three words that are used. Write a list of these three actions. Then write how God answers each action.

Action	Answer
1. _____	_____
2. _____	_____
3. _____	_____

Did you think it was easy to find the right answers in Matthew 7:7-8? You should find it easy to memorize these verses, although the passage is a little long. Start learning it now.

Think about the three words used to discuss prayer in Matthew 7:7-8.

Asking means requesting something you already know about. "Lord Jesus, I ask you to bring my friend to know your love." You already know about Christ's love. You now want your friend who is not a Christian to know about Jesus' love, too.

Searching means asking for an answer yo do not know about. "Lord Jesus, show me what I can do to show your love to my friend. I don't know what to do now."

Knocking means asking Christ to take care of something you cannot do, "Lord Jesus, serious sin problems in my friend's life have caused him not to want to hear about You. Please cause his heart to become open to You. Please show him how You can help him."

Read Matthew 7:9-11. These verses compare several gifts. Which comparison is the most important?

_____

The most important comparison in Matthew 7:9-11 is not about bread or stone, fish or snake. The most important is comparing earthly fathers who know how to take care of their children to the Heavenly Father. What do these verses tell you about God's answering when you ask, search, and knock?

_____

_____

Do you agree with this sentence explaining what Matthew 7:9-11 says? "If human fathers give what their children ask for, then the Heavenly Father will give even more." When you are thinking about the 5 & 5

Principle, what are you asking your Father to give you?

_____

You are asking your Heavenly Father to save five people whom you can only pray for. They will not let you share Christ with them.

Think about the three parts of prayer. What can you ask, search, and knock for today in your prayer for those five people?

1. Name _____   Ask: _____

   Search: _____   Knock: _____

2. Name _____   Ask: _____

   Search: _____   Knock: _____

3. Name _____   Ask: _____

   Search: _____   Knock: _____

4. Name _____   Ask: _____

   Search: _____   Knock: _____

5. Name _____   Ask: _____

   Search: _____   Knock: _____

Your Heavenly Father will answer your prayers. Watch and wait!

Week 10: The 5 & 5 Principle—
Five You Can Win By Prayer

Day 4: Prayer is Important

Read Matthew 14:23; Mark 1:35; Luke 6:12; 22:39-41.

Paul knew that prayer is important Write here a verse Paul wrote that proves Paul knew prayer is important.

_____

_____

_____

_____

(Philippians 4:6)

The Lord Jesus also knew that prayer is important. Write here a verse Jesus said that proves He knew prayer is important.

_____

_____

_____

_____

_____

(Matthew 7:7-8)

Now read Matthew 14:23; Mark 1:35; Luke 6:12; and Luke 22:39-41. These verses tell us where Jesus went to pray. You should be able to list three places.

1. _____

2. _____

3. _____

What time of day did Jesus choose for prayer time? You should be able to write two prayer times.

1. _____   2. _____

Jesus prayed on the mountain, in a place where He could be alone, and on the Mount of Olives. He prayed at night and at early morning. In your opinion, why did Jesus choose these times and places for prayer?

_____

Luke 22:41 might help you with the answer. Jesus walked away about as far as a stone can be thrown from His disciples (Luke 22:41). He chose times and places when He could be alone with God the Father. Which verse show you that prayer was a lifetime habit for Jesus?

_____

Did you notice the words "as usual" in Luke 22:39? How long did Jesus sometimes pray? Which verse tells you that?

_____

Luke 6:12 tells you that sometimes Jesus prayed all night. Think what this means. Jesus was always talking to God. Sometimes He needed time to get away from the pressure and to pray. The Lord Jesus felt it was necessary to have a habit of praying. What about you? Would you profit from this habit?

Look at your left hand. Think about the 5 & 5 Principle. What do you think would happen if you spent the same time in prayer for them that you would like to spend witnessing or studying the Bible with them?

Growing in Christ means having your priorities (what is important to you) in the right order. You did many things before you became saved that are now low priority (not important to you). You may need to make a careful decision to have time for prayer because old habits are hard to break. When and where do you—or will you—pray for your not-yet Christian friends? This is important. You may need to think about it today and to change it before tomorrow!

What could you cancel or change in your schedule that would give you a special time and place to pray for those five people who cannot be reached any other way?

_____

How much time will it require to tell Christ all the things about the five people? You need to ask, seek, and knock for them in your praying.

_____

Will you add these five people to your prayers during your regular Quiet Time? Or, will you have a different time for this?

_____

What will be the best place for you to have special prayer for your friends?

_____

What time of day will you pray for them?

_____

Then in God's time you will see prayer will change your friends. Is this serious to you? You will see them become curious about your faith in the Lord Jesus Christ. You will know personally the great power there is in prayer.

Week 10: The 5 & 5 Principle—
Five You Can Win By Prayer

Day 5: Prayer Brings Power to Win

Read John 14:13-14; Matthew 28:18-20.

Are you already using the 5 & 5 Principle in your life? Are you praying for five people who will not let you talk to them about Christ? Are you asking, seeking, knocking in your prayers as you tell Christ about the needs your five friends have? Write here the verse that tells you about these three parts to your praying.

_____

_____

_____

_____
(Matthew 7:7-8)

Jesus also taught people some other important things about praying. Read what Jesus says in John 14:13-14. Each verse tells you to ask for things in a special way when you pray. The teaching is given two times:

You are to ask in the name of _____ .
You make your requests in the name of Jesus whose power makes you free to work.

God the Father, who is all-powerful, will receive glory from Christ the Son when you pray in Jesus' name.

Now read Matthew 28:18-20. These verses tell us we have authority (power) when we pray in Jesus' name. How much authority?

_____

"All authority … in heaven and on earth." That is amazing! That means all that authority is for you when you pray in Jesus' name.

Hint: Matthew 28:18-20 is your memory verse for next week. It is also the longest passage to memorize since you began working in the *Survival Kit*. You might want to start working on this passage now.

Look at your hand. You have been using your hands to remember five people you can win by prayer and five you can win by witnessing. You have also been using your hands and fingers to remember what you have been learning in the *Survival Kit*. Write below what should be written on the palm of the hand, on the thumb, and on each finger. Do your best! On the next page, write the answers on the hand itself.

_____

_____

_____

_____

_____

_____

Check you answers to be sure you remembered everything correctly. Now think again about the five people who will not let you witness to them and the five people who will listen.

Learn a lesson from the 5 & 5 Principle. Have you decided it is easier to pray for people who will let you witness than for people who will not let you witness? Maybe you think that the five people you can only pray for will be the last to become saved because they are harder to reach.

Are they? You must not accept the idea that these five are harder to reach than the other five. What you think is hard or easy is very different to God. Your decisions about who is hard or easy will hurt your prayer life. You are asking the One with all power on earth and heaven to touch their lives when you pray in the name of Jesus for your friends.

The Bible tells us Saul of Tarsus was a powerful enemy of the early Christians. No one could witness to him. He was full of hate. He enjoyed causing trouble and pain to the Christians. But the power of Christ used a disciple's death and an encounter with Jesus Himself to cause Saul to be saved.

Do not think your prayers are weak for the five people who are hard and reject Christ. Never doubt He is able to do what you ask when you ask the Lord to enter a life through asking, searching, and knocking. In His name is all the power in the universe.

Week 11: The 5 & 5 Principle— Five You Can Win By Witnessing

Day 1: What it Means to Witness

Read Acts 1:8; John 15:26-27.

The 5 & 5 Principle:
Five you can win by prayer.
Five you can win by witnessing.

For the rest of your life keep the ten fingers on your hands full with people's names you are praying for and witnessing to. Always have in mind five people you are praying for and five people you are witnessing to. You will find that witnessing to five and praying for five is a full-time job for a Christian!

The word *witness* comes from the Greek word *marturia*. The English word *martyr* also comes from this Greek word. Many of the first people to share a witness for Jesus Christ died for doing so. This gave the word martyr its meaning. But the basic meaning of this word is "a person who gives proof."

Witnessing is not preaching. Witnessing is not teaching the Bible. Witnessing is giving proof or evidence. You have accepted Christ as your Savior and Lord. He has come to live in your life. You have prayed

for His Spirit to control you. Your personality has changed because of Christ in Your life. People who are around you can see the differences. You are a witness. You are living proof to people who are around you. Witnessing is not something you do as much as it is the result of Christ's living in you. His love is going through you to other people.

Jesus told His followers three things a little before He left earth in body and returned to heaven. He gave them a claim, a command, and a promise. All of these are found in Matthew 28:18-20 (your new memory passage.) You might be able to write these verses here. Try to do it now. Copy it carefully from the Bible if you can't write it from memory.

_____

_____

_____

_____

_____

_____

Now write an X beside the claim Jesus said in Matthew 28:18-20. You studied this claim last week when you were learning about the great power of prayer.

Did you find the claim Jesus gave to His followers? If so, you should also be able to find the promise Jesus gave in the last part of those verses. Everything between the claim and the promise is the command Jesus gave to His followers. Sometimes it is called the Great Commission.

Another important promise and command Jesus gave to His followers a little before He left this earth is found in Acts 1:8. Read that verse now. What did Jesus say must happen before the followers started to witness?

_____

Why was it necessary for Jesus' followers to have the Holy Spirit?

_____

Jesus named some areas in Act 1:8 where His followers were supposed to go to be witnesses in the power of the Holy Spirit. He started with Jerusalem, the city where they were at that time. Then He moved to areas farther away. Look at the four circles below. The center circle is finished. Fill in the other blanks in the circles on the left, following Jesus' words about witnessing in Acts 1:8.

The principle of Jesus' teachings about witnessing are still the same today. Write the name of your city in the center circle on the right. Write the name of your state in the blank for the next one. Write the name of your country in the third blank. On the last blank, write the same words as in the circle on the left.

Read John 15:26-27. What relationship in these verses (as in Acts 1:8) is emphasized before your witnessing for Christ begins?

_____

After studying Acts 1:8 and John 15:26-27, what do you think is the one most important thing required to become a witness for Christ?

_____

Is God's Holy Spirit living in your life today? _____

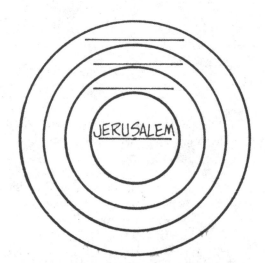

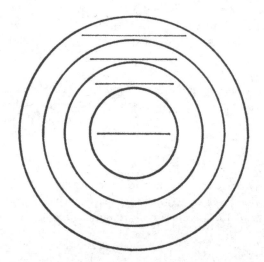

Week 11: The 5 & 5 Principle— Five You Can Win By Witnessing

Day 2: Christ Gives You Power

Read Ephesians 5:18; Acts 2:1-18.

You have memorized many verses about the Holy Spirit since staring the *Survival Kit*. Two of the memory verses in Galatians 5 tell about your new nature. Can you write both of them here?

_____

_____

(Galatians 5:16)

_____

_____

(Galatians 5:22-23)

You also have learned other memory verses that tells us God's Holy Spirit caused the Bible to be written. Can you write these verses from memory?

_____

_____

_____

_____

(2 Peter 1:20-21)

Now read another verse you have read before: Ephesians 5:18. Next read Acts 2:13-18. What two things are compared in both verses?

_____

Both Ephesians 5:18 and Acts 23:13-18 compare drinking wine with being filled by the Holy Spirit. Now read the entire story in Acts 2:1-18. What was required from the Christians for witnessing?

_____

Did you write that the *filling of the Holy Spirit* was the required thing? Now read carefully the two sentences below. Think again about Acts 1:1-18. Mark the correct sentence.

❏ The Holy Spirit gave these people a new inner experience. He did not expect them to talk about it. It was enough for them to be a silent witness.

❏ The first thing the Holy Spirit did after filling the people was to make it possible for them to speak their witness to people who were not saved so that all the people could hear about Christ.

The right answer is easy! Think about this one. What happens when a person drinks too much wine?

❏ The person becomes quiet.

❏ The person talks a lot.

What happens when a person is filled with the Holy Spirit of Christ?

Drinking wine and being filled with the Spirit are a good comparison. Both things cause people to talk, not to be quiet. What will witnessing involve for you as a person who has Christ living in you, controlling everything?

_____ Living for Christ but not talking about Him.

_____ Talking about Christ but not living for Him.

_____ Both living for and talking about Christ.

One way you can talk about Christ is by sharing Bible verses you know are true from your experience. First Peter 1:18-19 and Ephesians 2:8-10 are good examples. Try to write them from memory.

_____

_____

_____

_____

(1 Peter 1:18-19)

_____

_____

_____

_____

_____

(Ephesians 2:8-10)

Someone said that the biggest hypocrite in the world is a person who says: "I don't have to talk to other people about Christ. All people have to do is to see my actions. They'll know I am a Christian." We will talk about Him when self is no more the king and Christ becomes the King of our lives.

You may ask: "What is in my life that will be important to a person who is not saved? I know only a few things about the Christian life. I must wait until I learn more about the Bible to witness." Not true!

You have already experienced new life. Christ's Spirit lives in you. He fills you any time you ask. A witness is a person who gives proof. You have a lot of proof in your life as Christ lives through you.

Your five friends are open to listening to you. They are curious. Don't be afraid. Talk about what has happened in your life. Share your daily experiences with Christ. Talk about your living with Christ to the five people who are willing to listen to you. Do it today!

Week 11: The 5 & 5 Principle— Five You Can Win By Witnessing

Day 3: Saying Your Witness

Read Romans 1:16; Acts 22:1-15; 26:9-20.

Do you remember what the word *witness* means? It means a person who gives proof.

You have the proof of a changed life. Christ lives in you and controls everything. You need to speak your witness, to tell people who Christ is and what He has done for you. Say that He is now important in your life.

The apostle Paul knew how to say his witness. Paul spoke his witness whenever he had the opportunity. Paul said his witness to everyone who would listen to him. Read these words Paul wrote: "For I am not ashamed of the gospel, because it is the Gods power for salvation to everyone who believes." It is the way He saves men—if they put their trust in Him. Can you honestly say the same thing Paul said in Romans 1:16? This verse is your last memory verse in the *Survival Kit*. Do more than memorize it. Make it a part of your life.

There are two places in the Bible where you can find details of times Paul spoke his witness. Read Acts 22:1-15 and Acts 26:9-20.

Notice that both times Paul used his own experience in becoming saved as the proof for his witnessing. Both times he said four things about his salvation experience. These four things are written in the chart.

Write in the correct place below the numbers of the verses from Acts 22 in which Paul told about each of the four parts of his salvation experience. Then do the same thing with the verses in Acts 26. These answers will be in two to four verses in a row. All of these will be in order as you see them in the chart.

	Acts 22	Acts 26
1. Paul did not always follow Christ.	_____	_____
2. God started to speak to Paul.	_____	_____
3. Paul accepted Christ as His Lord.	_____	_____
4. Paul's new life focused on Christ's plan.	_____	_____

Answers:

Acts 22	Acts 26
v. 3-5	vv. 9-12
vv. 6-9	v. 19
vv. 10-13	vv. 13-18
vv. 14-15	vv. 19-20

You will be amazed to find that most unbelievers have never heard anyone share information the same way Paul shared. Every salvation experience is different. Your own testimony about how you became saved is personal and individual. It is proof no one else can give. No one else will have the same experience you have had.

You can share the same kind of information Paul shared. The information you share will sound different from the information Paul talked about. Your experience and Paul's experience are different.

Remember the five people you listed on the fingers of your right hand? They are people who are open to your sharing Christ. Write four things in the places below about your salvation experience that should be shared with your five people.

1. MY LIFE AND ATTITUDES BEFORE ACCEPTING CHRIST:

_____

_____

_____

2. HOW I UNDERSTOOD GOD WAS TALKING TO ME:

_____

_____

_____

3. HOW I ACCEPTED CHRIST (BECAME SAVED):

_____

_____

_____

_____

4. WHY BEING A CHRISTIAN IMPORTANT TO ME:

_____

_____

_____

_____

Don't misunderstand and think this means you must have enough information for a sermon. Witnessing is not preaching. Witnessing is giving proof You will find many opportunities to share a one-minute testimony of your salvation experience if you can develop it. Share it with someone right now!

Week 11: The 5 & 5 Principle— Five You Can Win By Witnessing

Day 4: The Personal Touch

Read Matthew 9:10-13; 1 Corinthians 9:19-23; John 4:40-41.

A few weeks ago you were not a Christian. Who or what had a strong influence to help you decide to become a Christian?

_____

Now read Matthew 9:10-11. What did people criticize Jesus for?

_____

Why do you think Jesus accepted criticism by being with evil people (sinners)? Read Matthew 19:12-13 before answering.

_____

Jesus came to call those who are sinners. He had loving-kindness for people who were spiritually sick. Now read what Paul wrote in 1 Corinthians 9:19-21. What did Paul mean?

❏ A. "It doesn't matter whom I fellowship with."

❏ B. "I agree with whomever I am with."

❏ C. "I decided to make friends with all kinds of people."

Sentence C is what Paul meant. This is Paul's feeling about making friends. Why did Paul think this was needed Read 1 Corinthians 9:22-23 before answering.

_____

Paul did it all to get the Good News to men. Paul knew that not everyone he made friends with would accept Christ. But Paul was willing to associate with everyone so he might lead some to Christ (1 Corinthians 9:22). He knew that God's power would save anyone who believed. Can you write from memory the verse Paul wrote to support this?

_____

_____

_____

(Romans 1:16)

Now read John 4:40-41. In Jesus' day Jews and Samaritans hated one another. Jesus was a Jew. What was Jesus willing to do when the Samaritans invited Him?

_____

What happened because Jesus was willing to stay two days with the Samaritans?

_____

Look now at the five fingers on your right hand. Your five friends are not like the Samaritans. They have not yet accepted Christ as Savior and Lord. Your friends might be afraid of the changes Christ would cause in their lives. Your friends might feel shy about leaving a life they are comfortable with to start a new life. (Did you feel like this?)

It is interesting to notice in the Book of Acts that every person who became a Christian had help from another Christian. Christ sent Peter to help a Roman soldier. He sent Philip to an Ethiopian government office. He sent Paul to Lydia and her friends to the jailer at Philippi, and to many other people. In every situation a personal touch was given.

Look again at your right hand. These five people are open to let you share with them. You should give time to them. Share your life with them. They don't have many other places to see the love of God coming through a person. They will see Christ's love in your words, your thoughts, and your life when you share with them. This will have a strong influence on them.

Priorities need to be straight. Look again at your schedule for every week. Is there time for those five people? What can be changed to make time for them? Pray about your answer during your Quiet Time.

_____

_____

Look now at your left hand. Are you still remembering to pray for those five people who are not open to let you share with them? What verses remind you of three ways to pray about them?

_____

_____

_____

_____

_____

(Matthew 7:7-8)

What verses remind you how much power you have when you pray?

_____

_____

_____

_____

(Matthew 28:18-20)

Week 11: The 5 & 5 Principle— Five You Can Win By Witnessing

Day 5: Pray and Witness

Read Matthew 18:19-20; Acts 2:41-47.

Most things about the Christian life are caught more than they are taught. Read Matthew 18:19-20. How many people does verse 20 talk about meeting together in the name of Christ ? _____

Verse 19 has a prayer promise that Christ gave us. What is it?

_____

Jesus will be there with two or three people who are gathered together in His name. Jesus promises to answer when two people agree about a request in His name. What does this mean when you think about the 5 & 5 people who are not yet saved? Do you know another Christian in your life who is more mature than you are? This may be someone you could pray with for the salvation of your 5 & 5 people.

Yes ❐   No ❐

Who can pray with you? _____

How would you feel if a mature Christian volunteered to help you by becoming friends with the five people on your right hand? How would you feel if this mature Christian helped you find ways to witness to these people?

_____

_____

Remember the person you thought of a moment ago to pray with you. Do you think this person would also help as a witness for Christ?

Yes ❐   No ❐

Most things about the Christian life are better caught than taught. Your Christian growth will be greater if you associate with other Christians who have had time to grow. Read now some verses you read several week ago when you studied about one Body, the Church. (See Acts 2:41-47.) Those Christians did not try to do it alone. They shared everything they had. They shared their lives with outer Christians in the church.

Think about how those church members' sharing must have influenced people who were not saved. Can your church have the same kind of witness to people in your community? Why or why not?

_____

When you are with other Christians, is it easier or harder to do what Paul said in Romans 12:16? _____

Say the verse now. Say it again every time you need new courage to share Christ with your friends.

Use your imagination to try to think what would happen if every Christian in the world would use the 5 & 5 Principle to reach ten people.

There is no reason you can't be one of the people who use this principle. But as you have seen again and again, you must carefully analyze your life if you want to really follow Christ as your Lord.

Now that you are a Christian, Christ wants to use your life for His purposes. He wants to improve your skills so that He can use you to reach the lost people in the world.

The most important thing about the 5 & 5 Principle is this: Your priorities must be changed. You cannot do whatever you want and also follow Christ.

For 11 weeks you have developed a new pattern in your life. You have added the *Survival Kit* to your daily schedule. But that is only the beginning. Christ has come to give you a new life. But in order for Christ to give you a new life, you must give Him your entire schedule. Some of the things you thought were necessary for yourself every day may go to the bottom of your list.

Is it worth it? Were you satisfied with your life before you became a Christian? No. Maybe it was that unhappiness that led you to give your life to Christ. Don't stop now! Let Christ have your life completely.

All Christ wants to do in you and for you will be through the Church, the Body of Christ. Your personal prayer and your witnessing should be related to the church's work. Those people whom you help become saved will become part of the Body. Let Christ plan your schedule and your priorities.

Where Do You Go From Here?

One of the first truths you learned in *Survival Kit* is the importance of being a part of the Body of Christ. To thrive and grow spiritually, it is essential that you be surrounded by others who are concerned about your spiritual growth. If you have not already joined a church and become involved in its fellowship and its Bible study and training ministry, you should do so at once.

You have established some habit patterns in your Quiet Time that are important to your spiritual growth: Bible reading, memorizing Bible verses, and prayer. This Quiet Time probably has become a natural part of your day. You have completed *Survival Kit*, but you realize that you are still at the beginning of your walk with Christ. These habits are absolutely essential to your continued spiritual growth.

Continue to read and study the Bible. Read a chapter at each Quiet Time. Then guide your meditation with questions like: *How would I have felt or what would I have done if I had been there? What is God saying to me through this passage? How should this passage affect the way I will live my life today?*

The Bible verses you have memorized are only the beginning of your learning. Twice each week select one or more verses from your Scripture readings. Continue to memorize and to review the way you have been doing since you started work in your *Survival Kit*.

The 5 & 5 Principle has taught you to pray for persons who need to come to know Christ. Use the same kinds of intercessory prayer for persons who have other needs and about other matters that are a real concern to you.

Your Christian growth has only just begun!